Preface

'The study has benefited from the excellent co-operation of authorities visited by the study team and those that took part in the detailed survey.'

In February 1995 the Audit Commission began a study of capital expenditure and acquisition. The study is being carried out in two phases. The Phase 1 report, *Just Capital* (Ref. 1), was published in September 1996. *Just Capital* examined the management of capital projects. It found considerable variation in the success with which local authorities manage their capital projects and identified both good and bad practice.

Research for Phase 1 involved:

◆ visits to a cross-section of authorities, examining their management of capital programmes, and looking in more detail at 21 separate projects;

◆ a postal survey of 60 authorities and the collection of information on more than 700 projects; and

◆ comparing local authority practice with that of the private sector.

Phase 2 of the study is considering how authorities acquire their capital resources. The study assesses the impact of national policy on the management of capital expenditure. It looks at increased access to European Union (EU) and other bid-led funding, and the Private Finance Initiative (PFI). The Phase 2 national report is scheduled for publication in mid-1997.

This handbook draws on the findings of the study programme to date. It provides practical guidance, examples and checklists on managing capital programmes and projects. It is aimed at senior local authority managers. The handbook examines eight aspects of programme and project management and complements the Phase 1 national report, *Just Capital*.

During 1996 and 1997 external auditors are reviewing how well local authorities manage their capital expenditure with a view to identifying opportunities for improvement. An audit guide has been produced to help auditors do this.

The study has been carried out by a team from the Local Government Studies directorate with support from Davis Langdon Consultancy. The Local Government Studies team comprised Max Peacock, on secondment from the Department of the Environment (DoE), and Carmel Zammit, initially under the direction of Jon Vaughan Jones and then Robert Hill. The Davis Langdon team consisted of Adrian Jackson-Robbins, Malcolm Potter and Paul Coomber, under the direction of Jim Meikle. A group of practitioners has provided valuable assistance by meeting to discuss and advise on key issues as they emerged, and commenting on drafts of the national report and the management handbook.

The study has benefited from the excellent co-operation of authorities visited by the study team and those that took part in the detailed survey. The Commission would like to take this opportunity to thank all those concerned.

Introduction

Capital projects are usually complex, posing significant management challenges. Each project is different, requiring the co-ordination of a wide range of people with differing skills and the availability of other resources such as equipment and materials. Site conditions and even bad weather can throw a project off course. Funding uncertainties add to the risks associated with capital projects and the regime of central controls can have important implications – particularly in influencing start dates and setting deadlines for completion. A number of developments in the construction industry, in local government and in the way expenditure is funded makes it even more of a challenge.

Construction industry changes

Local authorities face changes in the wider construction industry. Sir Michael Latham's report, *Constructing the Team* (Ref. 2), targeted an ambitious 30 per cent reduction in construction costs by the year 2000. These savings could be realised through efficiencies gained from a more effective partnership between industry and client, the use of new forms of contract and standard construction components (and other technical improvements), and the adoption of cost-reducing techniques such as risk and value management. The Construction Industry Board was set up to help with the detailed implementation of the report. To this end, a number of reports have been published (Appendix 1), but it is still too early to assess their impact.

Significant savings will be possible only if both clients and the industry work effectively together, avoiding the adversarial attitudes and practices that have been common. Central government has committed itself to the principles of Latham (Ref. 3), and to becoming a best-practice client. Some of the Latham recommendations have already been enacted in legislation (Ref. 4) (Appendix 2). The standard forms of contracts used by authorities will have to be revised to reflect the requirements of proposed regulations on a rapid and impartial adjudication process and a number of rights and responsibilities relating to payment.

Local government changes

Local government also faces major changes in the way in which it manages capital expenditure. Compulsory competitive tendering (CCT) for 'construction related services' (CRS) will affect professional services in all the larger authorities and, with the reduction of the threshold above which CCT applies, in an increasing number of smaller ones. The effect of CCT for CRS is likely to be profound. To prepare for CCT, many authorities are introducing service level agreements (SLAs), trading accounts, shadow business units, and in some cases they have voluntarily contracted out services.

In the longer term, service departments – which have tended to rely on a pool of in-house technical staff to 'tell us what we want' – will have to be more specific about what they actually want and what they are willing to pay for. Advice on construction matters may be available only at a price, encouraging better cost awareness, but possibly discouraging service departments from seeking professional advice, with attendant dangers. This new environment will pose challenges for the maintenance of good teamworking between departments.

Funding changes

The overall level of capital expenditure has declined in real terms in the 1990s (Exhibit 1), although local authorities in England and Wales still spend over £6 billion a year. Capital expenditure varies widely between authorities. County councils, London boroughs and metropolitan districts spend on average £39 million a year and non-metropolitan districts about £6 million. Although the figure for non-metropolitan districts is significantly lower, it represents a much larger proportion of their total expenditure because their budgets, unlike those of other authorities, do not include spending on education and social services.

Local authorities finance their capital expenditure in four main ways: by borrowing, by grants received from government and other sources, by selling land and property (capital receipts), and by using revenue funds (Exhibit 2, overleaf). Central government restricts the extent to which sales can be used to finance new spending. Government also either directs or strongly influences the timing and nature of spending financed through borrowing and grants by its allocation of resources between authorities. The acquisition of capital resources is the subject of Phase 2 of the Commission's study.

Other sources of funding are also important. For example, authorities have benefited by over £250 million in the first two years of the National Lottery, and European Union (EU) funding can account for up to 10 per cent of an authority's capital programme. From 1994 to 1996 authorities in England

Exhibit 1
Gross capital expenditure (at 1995/96 prices)

Overall spending has declined in real terms.

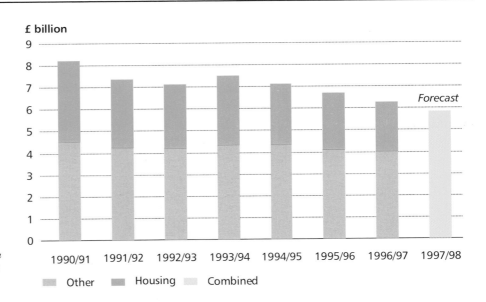

£ billion

Source: Audit Commission analysis of DoE data for local authorities in England. Deflated using GDP deflator. Breakdown between services for 1997/98 is not yet available.

Exhibit 2
Capital expenditure by source of finance

Over half the expenditure in 1995/96 is financed through borrowing and grants from central government.

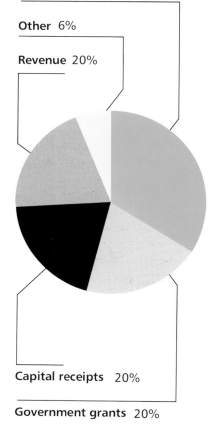

Borrowing (credit approvals) 34%

Other 6%

Revenue 20%

Capital receipts 20%

Government grants 20%

Source: Audit Commission analysis of DoE data

received 55 per cent of the £1,250 million available in the European Regional Development Fund (ERDF).

An increasing proportion of funding for capital expenditure is allocated on a competitive basis. In some cases the bidding is on a strategic basis such as the Housing Investment Programme (HIP), sometimes for groups of projects such as the Single Regeneration Budget (SRB) or the 'packages' in the Transport Policies and Programmes (TPP), and sometimes it is for a specific project (such as for National Lottery awards). Recently the Government has moved to piloting a corporate bidding process (Capital Challenge).

In addition, the Government is encouraging local authorities to develop new project using private sector finance, expertise and services. New regulations were introduced in autumn 1996 to facilitate the development of the private finance initiative (PFI) in local government.

Programme changes

The spending patterns of authorities have changed significantly over the years. More than two-thirds of construction projects consist of renovating existing dwellings (Exhibit 3). This change is most marked in housing, with very few new houses being built.

How to use this handbook

This handbook aims to promote the successful management of capital programmes and projects. The handbook is intended as a working document for use by senior managers with responsibilities for managing capital programmes and projects, or for parts of the process. The handbook will help managers to review their performance, to identify strengths and weaknesses and to make improvements. It includes self-diagnostic questions for examining performance, checklists of recommended practice, and case studies describing practices adopted by individual authorities. Each chapter ends with a checklist for action.

The handbook is a guide, not a prescriptive blueprint. Councils' circumstances differ; individual authorities and managers should use the handbook to identify areas where they can improve performance and develop their own solutions.

The handbook excludes consideration of the acquisition of capital resources, which will be examined in the Phase 2 national report. Nor does it cover CCT, which affects the provision of in-house construction-related services. However, the good practices described in this handbook will help in-house service providers review the services that they provide and their costs.

Structure of the handbook

There are a number of stages in delivering projects from getting started – when a project is first included in the capital programme – to completion and handover. The handbook does not examine each project stage in sequence but considers eight aspects of management (Box A, overleaf) which must be applied effectively if projects are to meet needs, be well designed, represent

Exhibit 3
Number of practical completions
during 1994/95

Over two-thirds of construction projects
consist of refurbishing existing buildings.

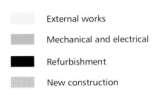

External works

Mechanical and electrical

Refurbishment

New construction

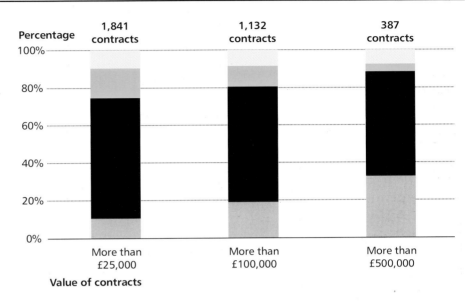

*Source: Audit Commission survey of construction
projects exceeding £25,000 in value*

value for money, be well managed during construction and provide lessons for
the future. Each of the eight chapters addresses one aspect of management:

♦ **Chapter 1: Programme and Bidding Management** – examines how
authorities can achieve maximum benefit from their capital expenditure by
managing their capital programmes and by bidding for funds effectively.

♦ **Chapter 2: Organisation Management** – identifies the essential
organisational and communication requirements for the delivery of
successful projects.

♦ **Chapter 3: Option and Design Management** – focuses on the
importance of allowing sufficient time for design and project planning, and
using tools such as value management and value engineering to achieve
value for money.

♦ **Chapter 4: Procurement Management** – considers how authorities can
systematically evaluate and select the most appropriate procurement
approach.

♦ **Chapter 5: Time Management** – identifies how projects can be delivered
on time.

♦ **Chapter 6: Cost Management** – considers how projects can be delivered
within budget.

♦ **Chapter 7: Risk Management** – examines how the systematic
identification of risks can help to achieve best value for money by avoiding
potential loss of time, money or other benefits.

♦ **Chapter 8: Quality Management** – examines how quality can be built
into projects and how post-project reviews can help to improve
performance.

Box A
Structure of the handbook

Handbook chapters	Project stages					
	Getting started	**Scope and approval**	**Detailed design**	**Tender**	**Delivering projects**	**Handover and review**
Programme and Bidding Management	– Property information – Deciding priorities – Planning ahead – Managing resources – Effective bidding	– Planning ahead			– Managing resources – Monitoring	– Programme reviews
Organisation Management	– Roles and responsibilities – Human resources – Organisational structure – Communications	– Human resources – Communications	– Human resources – Communications	– Human resources – Communications	– Human resources – Communications	– Human resources – Communications – Completion and administrative closure
Option and Design Management	– Making time to plan – Meeting needs – Project justification	– Making time to plan – Meeting needs – Project justification – Value management – Clear specification	– Making time to plan – Cost-effective design – Value engineering			
Procurement Management	– Procurement of technical services	– Procurement strategy – procurement system – Selection and appointment of consultants	– Procurement strategy – packaging/phasing construction work – Selection and appointment of consultants	– Procurement of construction services – Selection and appointment of subcontractors	– Procurement of construction services – Selection and appointment of subcontractors	
Time Management	– Project programme	– Project programme – Monitoring – Reporting	– Project programme – Monitoring – Reporting	– Project programme – Monitoring – Reporting	– Project programme – Monitoring – Reporting	– Project programme – Reporting
Cost Management	– Setting realistic project budgets	– Setting realistic project budgets – Cost of technical services – Reporting	– Setting realistic project budgets – cost planning – Cost of technical services – Reporting	– Setting realistic project budgets – Cost of technical services – Reporting	– Cost of technical services – Monitoring cost of construction – Reporting	– Monitoring cost of construction – Reporting
Risk Management	– Principles of risk management	– The practice of risk management – Selection of procurement option – Contingency planning	– Contingency planning	– Contingency planning	– Contingency planning	
Quality Management	– Quality management system – Quality planning – Assembling the right team	– Quality management system – Quality planning – Quality control during design	– Quality management system – Quality planning – Quality control during design	– Quality management system – Quality planning	– Quality management system – Quality planning – Quality control during construction	– Quality management system – Quality planning – Post-project review

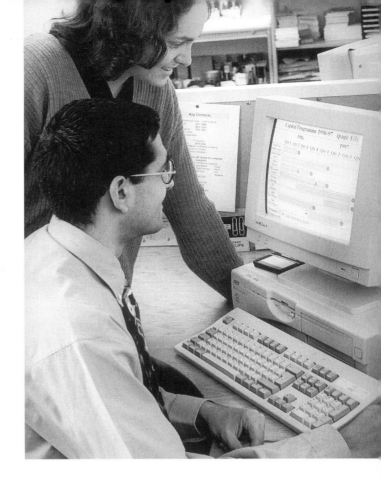

However well an authority manages its projects, it will achieve maximum benefit for the people it serves only if projects are carefully chosen and capital resources well managed. Authorities need to:

1   Programme and Bidding Management

- assess needs, appraise options and identify risks;

- prioritise competing demands on resources;

- identify and maximise sources of potential funding;

- deliver the highest priority projects; and

- regularly monitor and check the programme against objectives.

All local authorities have a programme of capital expenditure which consists of a number of projects. The programme should enable members to set priorities, define timescales, and identify the budgetary consequences – what will be spent, when, and where the money comes from. Uncertainty over the annual allocation of capital resources is often given as a reason for short-term planning and 'spend-up' syndrome. However, authorities can take steps to minimise the constraints of the capital system; some are more successful than others at doing this.

Some elements of the programme may be treated as discrete units. For example, departments such as highways or housing may manage their own programmes, largely in isolation from the corporate programme. However, a good programme will help authorities/departments to identify and deliver over time a range of projects that best meet local needs within available resources. A good programme will:

– be driven by needs;
– be based on sound information;
– contain rational processes;
– enable a flexible response;
– maximise value from resources used; and
– learn from experience.

These issues are considered in this chapter, and the following recommendations are made.

Authorities should:	This will have the following benefits:
◆ put in place corporate procedures to test that potential projects meet overall priorities and service strategies; reflect users' needs; identify time-critical elements of a project; and monitor the development of projects	◆ only capital projects that meet the criteria set by members will be included in the capital programme
◆ have, as a minimum, a planning horizon of three years	◆ allows time to plan projects
◆ maintain a property database that includes stock condition and usage data	◆ identification of: (i) potential projects; and (ii) surplus assets available for disposal
◆ develop partnerships with other public bodies; voluntary organisations and the private sector	◆ generate additional resources to enhance the capital programme; develop alternative approaches to meet needs
◆ identify and bid for other external sources of capital finance on a co-ordinated basis	◆ generate additional resources
◆ review their procedures for monitoring and reporting on the performance of the capital programme	◆ prompt action to resolve issues; improved capital planning process

Principles of capital programme management

♦ What does effective capital programme management involve?

1.1 Authorities operate to an annual cycle of capital control associated with their own revenue budgeting and with central government's capital allocation process. But the most effective programme managers are not restricted to the routine of an annual cycle. They have a longer term goal but operate flexibly within it as potential projects develop, suitable funding becomes available and as ongoing projects complete early or run into difficulties of time or cost. In such circumstances, the annual cycle has two main functions: it establishes and revises the longer term goals, and it holds the programme manager to account for delivering projects that will meet them.

1.2 The Audit Commission's survey measured the performance of projects which had reached practical completion in 1994/95 and for which information was available, against a set of indicators. The indicators sought to identify:

♦ poor planning – by measuring the difference between the estimated construction costs at scheme design or pre-tender stage, and the successful tender sum;

♦ late changes in design – by identifying differences between the successful tender sum and the contract sum;

♦ cost overruns and underruns – by measuring the difference between the contract sum and the outturn; and

♦ time overruns – by measuring the actual construction period against the period specified in the contract.

1.3 The seven authorities[1] that scored best against the four indicators consistently provided more information about their programme management than the worst performers. They made more use of stock condition information and were significantly more likely to have a complete property database. The best performers were also more likely to use centralised management of external consultants, and longer planning horizons. There were no consistent differences between the two groups in respect of the balance between centralised and devolved internal management, or on survey questions about other performance or organisational criteria.

1.4 The analysis of a wide range of data about projects and about programme management processes, described in this management handbook, shows that there is no single process that drives overall performance, or makes sure that everything works well. But authorities that:

♦ know their property stock;
♦ decide their priorities;
♦ plan ahead;
♦ manage their financial and professional resources and monitor their use;
♦ review their programmes; and
♦ bid effectively are more likely to have good project outputs.

'...the most effective programme managers are not restricted to the routine of an annual cycle.'

[1] Two metropolitan districts; one London borough; three counties and one district council.

Property information

- Are we making the best use of our property?

1.5 All authorities need to pay attention to the strategic management of their property (Ref. 5) to ensure that they get the best use from it. Some authorities have used property reviews and strategic property management to help them target their capital resources (Case Study 1.1). New methods of capital accounting and the introduction of asset registers are increasing the pressures on authorities to review their properties strategically.

1.6 Although almost all the authorities in the Commission's survey claim to possess a database with information about their property, only about half record any details about the condition of their buildings (Exhibit 1.1) and fewer than 40 per cent of authorities use their property database to help them identify potential capital projects (Exhibit 1.2).

1.7 Those authorities which have carried out full condition surveys and put the information on computer are able to produce objective schedules of planned maintenance, and examine the merits of alternative strategies. For example, where they include details of standard components on their system, they can assess the implications of using replacements with a longer or shorter life.

Case Study 1.1
Property reviews

Systematic area property reviews lead to better use of the authority's property.

Since the mid-1980s Essex County Council has operated a system of area property reviews:

- to achieve a better match between users' requirements and the accommodation available to enhance the provision of services;
- to minimise property running costs; and
- to generate capital receipts, which could fund improvements.

The review method used in each area is to:

- assemble basic data – making judgements as to the detail needed to justify management decisions;
- identify service property problems and opportunities – with input from chief officers;
- prioritise problems and determine strategy – concentrating resources on the main issues rather than trying to look at every council property in the area;
- examine service needs – by discussion between local service officers and property services officers;
- prepare detailed data – as specific issues are addressed, more detailed data is added to the database to allow in-depth appraisal of options;
- formulate and analyse options;
- make recommendations on preferred options – these can be put to the relevant committees before the end of the review process to ensure that action is taken as early as possible; and
- undertake feasibility studies and implementation – possibly over several years.

The process has helped the authority to take a cross-departmental view of its property and to use it as effectively as possible.

UNIVERSITY OF WOLVERHAMPTON
Harrison Learning Centre

ITEMS ISSUED:

Customer ID: 7605351596

Title: Rome wasn't built in a day : a management handbook on getting value for mone
ID: 7623201886X
Due: 25/04/2009 23:59

Total items: 1
04/04/2009 17:28
Total Items on Loan: 4
Overdue: 0

Thank you for using Self Service.
Please keep your receipt.

Overdue books are fined at 40p per day for 1 week loans, 10p per day for long loans.

Exhibit 1.1
Property database

Half of all authorities have no readily accessible details on the condition of their properties.

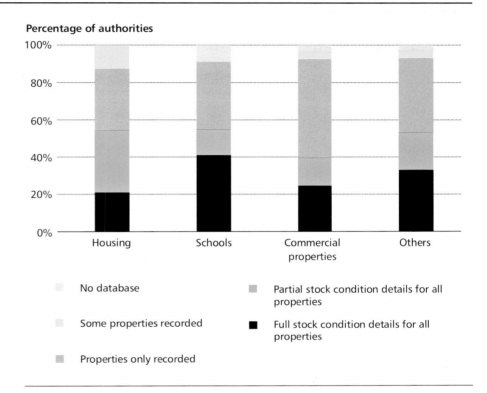

Percentage of authorities

- No database
- Some properties recorded
- Properties only recorded
- Partial stock condition details for all properties
- Full stock condition details for all properties

Source: Audit Commission survey

Exhibit 1.2
How authorities use their database

Fewer than half of the authorities that have a property database use it to help plan their capital expenditure.

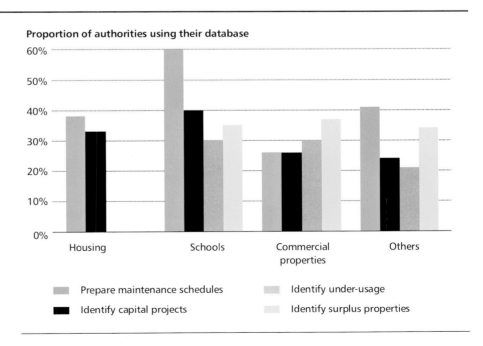

Proportion of authorities using their database

- Prepare maintenance schedules
- Identify capital projects
- Identify under-usage
- Identify surplus properties

Source: Audit Commission survey

1.8 Although authorities generally recognise the value of such information systems, many have not put them in place. For example, half of the local education authorities (LEAs) in the Commission's survey do not hold full data on the condition of their school buildings. In some cases, authorities regarded condition surveys and information systems as slow to complete, expensive to maintain and of limited value when resources are tightly constrained. In one authority which did not have information from condition surveys, a major refurbishment scheme was affected when the contractor started on site to discover that many of the roof timbers were affected by wet rot. In the absence of information, no consideration had been given to roof repairs when planning the scheme. The extra cost was estimated at between £400,000 and £500,000.

1.9 Without adequate information on stock condition, resources may be spent on an ad hoc basis, often with the resources going to the most articulate groups rather than to the areas that need them most. One large metropolitan district found that lack of rational planning had led to changes of direction in the programme, and resource allocation had been skewed by pressure from articulate groups. For example, one block of flats was refurbished because of a strong campaign by a tenants' group and local members. The refurbishment was 'needed', but the authority could not identify whether there was a higher priority for the money because it had no stock condition information. Also, some authorities are facing legal claims for compensation in respect of health problems caused by substandard housing. It is therefore vital that they know the state of their housing stock to enable them to target their resources and avoid costly legal challenges.

Deciding priorities

♦ Do we have processes which help us to identify priorities?

1.10 Extended planning horizons (see below) and sound information on the availability and the condition of property are not ends in themselves. Their purpose is to help authorities to make best use of limited resources by adopting rational processes for identifying priorities within their capital programmes.

1.11 Rational decision processes are needed at officer and member level (Case Studies 1.2 and 1.3). As well as helping to decide priorities, they are also useful for monitoring progress and learning from experience. The approach adopted will vary depending on the size and structure of the authority (Exhibit 1.3). Results from the Commission's Phase 2 questionnaire show that two-thirds of authorities have a group of officers which assesses and audits internal bids before they are recommended for inclusion in the capital programme. Sixty per cent of authorities use a standard format for this purpose. The agenda for such officer groups typically includes:

♦ assessing and agreeing recommended priorities for new projects (Chapter 3);

♦ monitoring progress against cost and time for ongoing projects, recommending action where necessary to avoid hold-ups;

Case Study 1.2
Essex County Council

Rational decision processes are needed at member level.

Essex County Council has found that a small group of experienced members is helpful in dealing with strategic issues and setting overall priorities. The group also reviews options before they are put to the authority's Policy and Resources Committee.

Case Study 1.3
London Borough of Hillingdon

Rational decision processes are needed at officer level.

In the London Borough of Hillingdon, an interdepartmental team of officers rigorously reviews all projects for compliance with the authority's priorities and for likely value for money before entering them into the capital programme. This process helps to ensure consistency with the authority's aims and to develop more effective teamwork and share experience across departments.

Exhibit 1.3
Rational decision process

Essex County Council uses a cycle of bidding, monitoring and review.

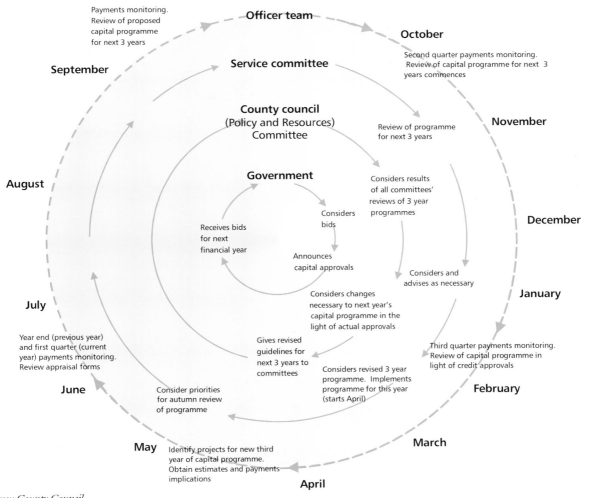

Source: *Essex County Council*

◆ approving short-term changes to the programme, and to bring forward shelf schemes; and

◆ reviewing lessons from finished projects.

1.12 Usually this group will report to the officers' management team, which reports to the committee or subcommittee of members responsible for the corporate programme. This committee will also be responsible for recommending to the council the allocation of capital resources between services and for taking a corporate view of bids for funding that are made to central government or other potential funders.

1.13 Rational planning mechanisms will also help authorities to gain most from central government programmes such as Housing Investment Programmes (HIPs) and Transport Policies and Programmes (TPPs). These programmes encourage authorities to plan strategically and review their plans rigorously each year. This imposes a helpful discipline on authorities' planning processes. However, HIPs and TPPs are based on single services, and authorities need to take specific steps to ensure that such service plans do not operate in isolation from overall corporate priorities and objectives.

Planning ahead

◆ How well do we plan our projects?

◆ Have we got clear and agreed procedures for signing off projects at each stage?

Forward planning

1.14 It takes several years for most major capital projects to progress from inception to completion. The traditional procurement route (Chapter 4) requires service decisions, initial design, planning consent and detailed design before an authority is ready to go to tender. Timescales may be shorter if the authority uses non-traditional procurement methods such as design and build, in which a contractor is appointed to design a building as well as build it. Also many refurbishment projects are phased over several years, either for technical or financing reasons.

1.15 As a minimum, capital programmes must include the commitments inherited from previous years and the impact of current year decisions on future years' spending. Over half of all authorities plan on a three- to five-year basis, but one in four plans for just one year at a time (Exhibit 1.4).

1.16 The annuality of central government allocations, and the consequent longer term uncertainty, represent constraints on long-term planning. Some authorities argue that these constraints make it impractical to plan more than a year ahead. Yet planning ahead is one way in which authorities can establish their strategic direction and deliver projects which progress towards it. In a climate of constraint on public sector capital expenditure, effective forward planning can help authorities make the most of what is available. It also provides a sound basis for preparing bids for external funding.

1.17 About half of all authorities report that they plan ahead for three years or more. They produce a programme containing prioritised potential capital projects for at least three years ahead, rolling the plan forward by one further year at each budget-setting round. They assess:

Exhibit 1.4
Planning horizons

One in four authorities plans for only
one year at a time.

Number of years authorities plan for

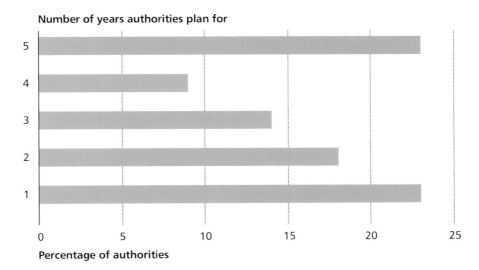

Percentage of authorities

Source: Audit Commission survey

Note:
13 per cent of authorities use different planning horizons for each service

- the commitments that previous decisions have created and how long the spending will continue;
- the implications of current decisions for spending in the following years; and
- their priorities within and between services, so that they can respond appropriately if future resourcing is higher or lower than assumed or if planned projects slip, providing an opportunity to bring forward projects from later years.

Approval to plan

1.18 Once an authority has decided that a potential project represents the best way of meeting a defined need, and so should be given some level of priority within the programme, formal approval should be given for work to begin on planning the project. Formal approval should involve users and project managers, as well as programme managers, 'signing off' any project justification document. Although some fieldwork authorities have robust approval mechanisms that enable planning of a project to begin once it has entered the programme, others do not allow detailed design to begin until funding for the project is secure. This apparent caution can lead to unplanned risks when preparatory work on the project is rushed to meet funding deadlines.

1.19 Affordability remains important. Expenditure on planning and design must be balanced against the level of resources likely to become available. Authorities will not want to waste resources on designing projects that are unlikely to be built and then be unable to deliver projects that should be affordable. But skimping on time for design is also a significant risk. Having projects ready is good planning because it enables an authority to benefit from time-limited funding if it becomes available late in the year. Authorities should therefore aim to begin planning early where projects have a realistic prospect of being included in the programme within two or three years, even though funding may be uncertain at the design stage.

1.20 Approval to plan is just that: approval to undertake more detailed planning; not to start work on site. It authorises the project manager to spend money on planning, but further review is required before giving approval to start on site.

Start approval

1.21 After a project receives approval to plan, it will progress until it is ready for tenders to be invited. A further formal review by the officer(s) responsible for managing the capital programme (the programme manager) will be necessary at this stage before deciding whether or not to proceed. The review should confirm whether the project still addresses the authority's priority needs (Chapter 3), and whether the resources available are sufficient – but not excessive – for its purpose (Chapter 6). The review should be carried out in conjunction with end-users, the client department and project manager, as well as with technical experts. Once tenders have been opened, there is then a final check of the available resources and the tender prices quoted, before the programme manager can give a final decision to proceed. Managing individual projects is addressed in Chapters 2 to 8.

Managing resources

- Are we monitoring our capital programme effectively?
- Can we bring forward projects if we are likely to underspend?
- Can we create a buffer in our capital budget to give us greater flexibility?

Monitoring

1.22 Most authorities' capital outturn is significantly different from their capital budgets. Data from the Commission's survey indicates that about half of authorities underspent or overspent their capital budgets by more than 10 per cent in at least two of the last three years. With the availability of capital being restricted, such budget performance is poor and reinforces the case that better programme management is needed. Failure to meet budgets casts doubts on the success of such authorities in effectively managing their resources to meet real needs. Some authorities monitor progress closely and build in flexibility to their programme management. They have consistently been able to deliver programme outturns close to their budgets.

1.23 Three-quarters of the authorities that responded to the Commission's Phase 2 questionnaire said that they had a group of officers which monitors the delivery of the capital programme on a corporate basis. However, the way that such groups work varies. In some shire districts there are powerful informal mechanisms, where relevant officers meet regularly and, with the benefit of long experience and mutual trust, are able to keep their programme on track with very little fuss. Other authorities, particularly larger ones, require more formal arrangements. But as a minimum, the programme manager and the management team should monitor monthly actual expenditure against the budget (Exhibit 1.5) and committed expenditure against planned commitments. Any slippage will immediately be apparent. Similarly, they

Exhibit 1.5
Capital programme

The programme manager should monitor actual expenditure and commitents against the budget and planned commitments.

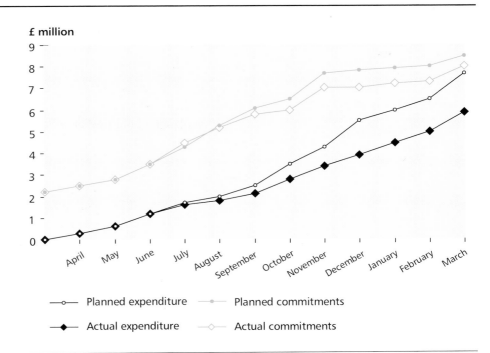

£ million

| | Planned expenditure | Planned commitments |
| Actual expenditure | Actual commitments |

Source: Thurrock District Council

should monitor milestone dates for each project and report to members two to four times a year.

1.24 Members need to be kept aware of significant changes to the programme and should be able to act quickly in the event of major problems on individual projects, because these may become more difficult and expensive to resolve if decisions are delayed. Half of the authorities that responded to the Commission's questionnaire have a separate subcommittee to monitor the capital programme. But members should normally avoid involvement in the management of individual projects. An exception would be where a political or strategic decision is required – such as in carrying out a major regeneration scheme with external partners and authority-wide implications, where members must represent the authority.

1.25 Authorities often face the position where they are under pressure to spend money by a fixed date, usually because it is a condition attached to some or all of the funding. Many authorities respond to such pressures by resorting to 'spend-up' syndrome. They try to accelerate the delivery of projects, often falling victim to the tendency of non-technical people – members and officers – to underestimate the time needed to plan projects properly and the risks involved if proper planning is skimped. In some cases auditors have found authorities that overvalue work completed at the year end or that anticipate payments by writing cheques in advance and keeping them in the safe until contractors have completed work to meet their value. Such actions jeopardise both probity and value for money.

'Authorities that use revenue balances or generate capital receipts are better able to cope with the constraints of annual allocations.'

1.26 But other authorities succeed in responding to pressures to spend quickly without jeopardising the emphasis on value for money. They manage their programmes actively, so that they can bring forward some projects and delay others as required. In addition, they build in flexibility to help them cope with changing circumstances. Their flexibility takes two forms – generating alternative projects and using unallocated resources when budgeting.

Alternative projects

1.27 There are many benefits to undertaking feasibility studies and project design before schemes enter the programme, such as minimising expensive, late changes. But having some projects which are sufficiently developed to proceed without delay also means that, should others slip, they can be substituted at short notice. Good practice authorities have a range of projects 'on the shelf', of different sizes and with different timescales, ready to be brought forward.

1.28 Funding of early planning work will need to be charged to revenue budgets in the first instance. However, once approval for a scheme is confirmed and capital funding identified, design costs may then be capitalised, although such expenditure cannot be treated as capital if a project is subsequently aborted (Ref. 6).

Flexible budgeting

1.29 Authorities that use revenue balances (housing or general fund) or generate capital receipts are better able to cope with the constraints of annual allocations. It gives them a buffer by allowing projects to be delayed or brought forward.

1.30 Not all local authorities have significant revenue or receipts to use. Tight capping ceilings and low availability of capital receipts make it more difficult to manage annual allocations and can impair the capital planning process seriously. However, housing authorities also have the flexibility to use housing revenue monies to fund housing capital projects. The limitation is the level of rents that members are prepared to set and the impact of recent housing benefit changes on the level of rent increases that authorities can implement. Whatever their situation, authorities need to strike a balance between the need to maintain or build reserves that allow flexibility and their requirements for immediate spending. This may require self-imposed restraint on spending in the short term to enable a more effective longer term programme.

Professional services

◆ Do we consider the need for professional skills when we plan our capital programme?

1.31 Planning the use of professional people is an important part of managing the delivery of capital programmes, balancing the needs of the programme with the availability of skilled people. But there was no evidence that fieldwork authorities gave it a high priority. While some technical departments may carry out such planning internally, it did not appear to be a part of the corporate programme planning process in any authority: one authority, which was able to expand its capital programme after years of tight restrictions, ran into problems in spending and monitoring its programme because it no longer employed enough technical staff, and had not engaged additional technical resources from external sources. The way that professional resources are managed in respect of each project is covered in Chapter 2: Organisation Management.

1.32 Evidence from both the survey and fieldwork does not show whether centralised or decentralised management of in-house professional staff works best. Neither is there any evidence that suggests that in-house staff or consultants are cheaper. However, some authorities rely almost entirely on in-house professional staff (Exhibit 1.6). Such an arrangement may not represent good value for money, particularly if the capital programme fluctuates from year to year or is contracting at a rate which is greater than the reduction in staff numbers. A changing mix of projects can similarly represent poor value for money if skills different from those available in-house are required. Authorities should avoid staffing for peaks and use short-term contracts or external consultants to make up shortfalls in the provision of professional services.

Exhibit 1.6
In-house professional fees as a percentage of total fees paid in 1993/94 and 1994/95

Some authorities rely almost entirely on their in-house professional staff for technical services.

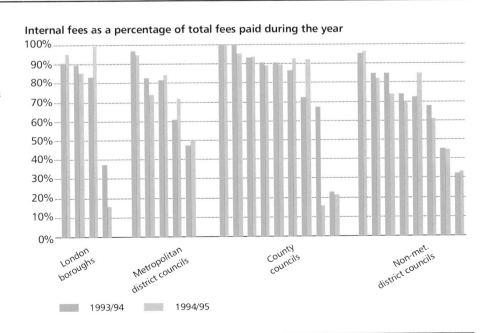

Internal fees as a percentage of total fees paid during the year

1993/94   1994/95

Source: Audit Commission survey

Programme reviews

◆ Do we review our programme to improve our performance?

1.33 Having made good plans, and worked effectively to put them into practice, authorities also need to carry out formal reviews of the success of their programmes. Programme reviews have two purposes:

◆ they provide a means of accountability, in showing how far the authority has done what it set out to do, and how much it cost; and

◆ they enable the authority to learn from experience. This covers identifying how well projects met client and user requirements, recording issues that might require changes to procedures and transferring lessons between different departments and types of project.

1.34 Authorities should take into account the results of reviews of past projects (Chapter 8), as well as the current state of ongoing projects. Good programme reviews will provide a foundation to help authorities decide programme priorities as funds for new potential capital projects become available.

1.35 Such reviews should also include reports on progress made in clearing final accounts from completed projects, since taking a long time to settle accounts can be an indicator of poor quality outcomes and poor project management.

1.36 With constraints on capital likely to remain a feature of local government life for the foreseeable future, most authorities would gain from a systematic review of the way in which they manage their capital programmes.

Effective bidding

◆ How can we bid for funds effectively?

◆ Have we got the right project?

◆ Do we understand the bidding competition?

◆ Are we working with the funder?

◆ Have we addressed corporate issues satisfactorily?

◆ Are we presenting our case well?

◆ What can we learn from our experiences?

1.37 An increasing proportion of funding for capital expenditure is bid-led. In some cases the bid is on a service basis (HIP and TPP); sometimes it is for a specific project(s) (that is, lottery or Single Regeneration Budget [SRB]) and recently it has been on a corporate basis (Capital Challenge). The capital planning arrangements, as described in the paragraphs above, should stand an authority in good stead. But there are a number of other issues that authorities need to consider:

◆ the choice of projects and partners;

◆ the bidding competition;

◆ working with the funder;

◆ corporate co-ordination;

◆ resourcing the bid; and

◆ presenting the bid.

Choosing projects and partners

1.38 Good preparation is essential for bids to succeed. The emphasis of nearly all bid-led funding is on forming partnerships with local businesses and other public sector organisations, and on community involvement. A major consideration for authorities is finding suitable partners who will be committed to seeing a bid through to the end. But forming partnerships takes time. Involving the community also takes some effort, particularly if there is no history of community involvement in capital projects.

1.39 Authorities responding to a survey for the second phase of the Commission's study found that sharing goals and objectives was the single most important thing in making partnerships work (Exhibit 1.7) and the lack of them was most likely to jeopardise a partnership (Exhibit 1.8).

1.40 Once partners have been found and projects identified, authorities need to prepare their business case (Chapter 3). This will include an assessment of the risks involved (Chapter 7). Authorities will also need to think laterally and consider ways in which projects can be improved, while at the same time ensuring that proposals are realistic and maximising funding from other sources (Case Study 1.4, overleaf).

Exhibit 1.7
Factors resulting in effective partnerships

The most important thing in making partnerships work is having shared goals and objectives.

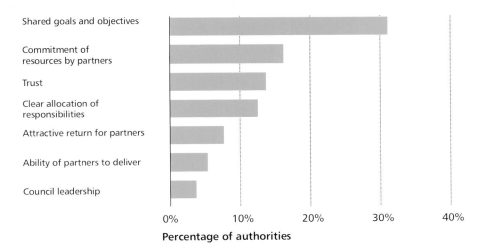

Source: Audit Commission survey

Exhibit 1.8
Factors resulting in unsatisfactory partnerships

The most significant thing that can jeopardise a partnership is a situation where the partners have different or unrealistic objectives.

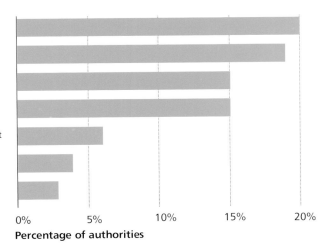

Source: Audit Commission survey

Case Study 1.4
The Peckham Pulse Health and
Leisure Centre

Lottery funding, coupled with an
innovative approach, enabled Southwark
to provide a much-needed facility.

Southwark Council was keen to make good a long-standing leisure deficiency – the lack of a modern swimming pool in an area of high population density and great social need. As part of a major urban regeneration programme leisure services officers used Lottery funding to develop a combined leisure and community health facility. They:

- ◆ formed a partnership with the local health authority, who paid for some of the design costs and for a moveable floor;
- ◆ allowed the health authority usage-time and space for health uses such as physiotherapy and community health promotion;
- ◆ actively encouraged private sector operators to run the fitness, children's play and catering services as well as providing capital finance for equipment;
- ◆ established a management structure which allows the local community a say in running the centre through an advisory board; and
- ◆ set up a project evaluation team to monitor the achievements of the centre, including building performance.

The project has been a success, with better facilities and higher rates of use, as well as contributing to a better built environment.

The bidding competition

1.41 Understanding and complying with the aims of the bidding competition is critical to the success or otherwise of a bid. Authorities identified this as the critical factor when putting a bid together (Exhibit 1.9). However obvious it may seem, the rules of the competition should be read very carefully. Government offices suggest that many bids that authorities submit clearly fall outside published criteria. But authorities should also consider whether they have identified the right funding source or whether another source might be more appropriate.

Exhibit 1.9
Putting together a bid

The most critical factor when putting
a bid together is understanding and
complying with the aims of the
competition.

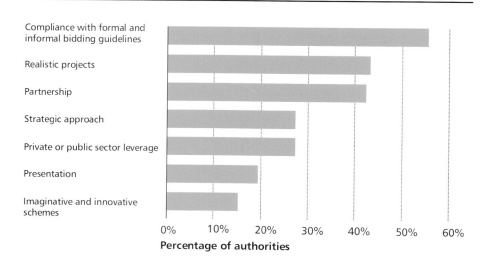

Source: Audit Commission survey

Sheffield thought carefully about the competition that they were entering.

Sheffield City Council chose a Capital Challenge bid that built on experience gained from previous SRB projects. The bid was multi-service and included elements of economic regeneration, in a focused geographical area. Experience of building partnerships, involving the community and local members, and making spending more effective by cross-service working was used to the full.

The Council recognised that Capital Challenge was a different type of competition which would require some differences in approach. In preparing the bid it:

- noted that only capital funding was available and that support would last for only three years. This led it to choose an area including a pre-war housing estate, which was the highest need of its type, rather than one of the most economically deprived areas of the City that would require a longer term strategy and accompanying revenue programmes to achieve effective and lasting results – Sheffield has mounted parallel SRB bids to try to address some of these needs;

- bid for a realistic amount – taking into account the outline amount available to the regional Government Office and Sheffield's likely share of this on a formula distribution. The bid was aimed at 25 per cent above the 'formula' level, with a reduced option at just below it; and

- produced the corporate strategy for capital investment required by the competition. Because this drew on existing service strategies and on the City-wide regeneration strategy produced by the City Liaison Group of local partners in Sheffield, it required relatively little new work.

The bid was successful in winning nearly £11 million of Capital Challenge funding.

1.42 Bids should reflect agreed corporate strategies that are aimed at meeting the needs of the community. Bids will be favoured if they fit in with county-wide, regional and national strategies, such as those for planning and land use. And authorities should also be aware of the European Union strategies that are likely to influence some government policies.

1.43 Authorities should use their network of contacts with other authorities to keep track of similar bids in neighbouring areas. And with Lottery-based projects they should also monitor any bids coming from unexpected sources in their area. A rival bid may lessen the chances of winning for both bidders, but a joint bid or one that draws out the differences between the bids is likely to be more successful. Authorities should attempt to discuss options with rival bidders rather than maintaining a distance.

1.44 The timescales involved are also critical. They will have implications for partners, for resourcing the bid, for consultation within the authority and externally, and for planning and implementation (Case Study 1.5). And inherent risks, such as an appeal against a compulsory purchase order, which can set back a project, need to be identified and assessed. Finally, the need for matched funding must be identified and appropriate provision made in the capital programme.

Working with the funder

1.45 Even when the rules of the bidding competition seem clear, it is worth talking to the funder about them. Sometimes terminology can be misleading. Discussions with the funder should help the bidder to get a picture of the underlying purpose of the competition. They will also help authorities adapt their bids to meet more of the funder's objectives or package them in a more acceptable way (Case Study 1.6). But bids must not be out of proportion to the funds likely to be available.

1.46 Discussions with the funder may suggest alternative approaches. The funder will have some expertise and will usually be basing their advice on other schemes that they have seen or funded. Authorities should be open to suggested alternative approaches, but they should consider them critically. Not all suggestions will be right in their circumstances.

1.47 The competition will often involve an interactive process between the funder and the bidder, with the project and bid developing iteratively. Authorities should be pro-active and take command of the process – funders are likely to form judgements about the bidders during this stage which could stand them in good stead when the bids are formally submitted. Authorities may well find that the funder has suggestions that go beyond the official rules of the competition. But they have to be balanced against locally identified needs, the requirements of other funders and what is realistically possible.

Case Study 1.6
The London Borough of
Southwark's leisure department

The team's approach ensures that its bid 'covers all the angles' and makes it easy for funders to see that their objectives are being met.

The London Borough of Southwark has a team of three leisure officers which is responsible for preparing bids, seeking partners and negotiating with potential funders. The team also provides advice to others in the authority who are preparing bids in new areas. It takes a pro-active, marketing approach to selling a project to potential private sector partners and to try and find mutually beneficial solutions.

Bids to funders such as the Government Office for London are closely scrutinised and cross-checked by team members to ensure that:

- the presentation of the bid makes it clear how it meets the competitive criteria;

- the bid fits in with the authority's own service and corporate strategies and with published regional strategies and planning guidance;

- the bid demonstrates how it meshes in with government and other funder policy objectives – for example, by referring to published policy statements and to recent ministerial speeches; and that all options are explored – for example, by suggesting:
  - possible links with other current bids;
  - other potential partners and funders; and
  - risks in the bid and options for managing them.

The aim is to present a coherent bid which explicitly recognises all the likely government concerns.

Some authorities have developed formal structures and procedures for ensuring bids are co-ordinated at a corporate level.

The Council has established a 'Funding Opportunities Group', consisting of senior officers drawn from each service department, which covers policy areas for which EU funding is potentially available. The group plays a key role in disseminating information about potential funding sources and in co-ordinating bids. It develops an overall programme for consideration by the chief officers management team, followed by a working party of senior elected members, before being submittted to the Policy and Resources Committee for approval.

1.48 In some cases the funder may, informally, suggest radical alterations or may give some broad advice on the type of scheme that will be looked at favourably. Informal advice should be taken with care. Personnel changes can make a difference to the status of the advice being given. Authorities should ensure that the advice is from a suitably senior source and that radical changes are not based on a single person's comments.

Corporate co-ordination

1.49 Authorities have adopted a range of internal procedures for working up and co-ordinating bids. In some authorities, bids are led by service departments. Many of these authorities have not allowed for matched funding in their capital programmes. In particular, there have been cases where the combined need for matched funding has exceeded the resources available from capital budgets or other external sources. In other instances, department-led bids have not complied with corporate priorities.

1.50 In order to avoid these problems, a number of authorities have developed structures and processes to ensure that:

◆ bids match corporate priorities;

◆ the progress of bids through the appraisal process is monitored; and

◆ appropriate plans are made for the provision of matched funding.

Some authorities do this informally through the chief officers' management team. Others have a more formal inter-departmental working group and/or (sub)commmittees (Case Study 1.7). And specialist internal bidding units to handle all bidding applications have proved effective in authorities involved with a number of bids.

Resourcing the bid

1.51 Nearly nine out of ten authorities surveyed for Phase 2 of the Commission's capital expenditure study said that the demand for matching funding had increased over the last three years, and one-third of them said that it had had a significant impact on their capital programmes. Some authorities have established a 'matching fund pool' within the capital budget. The pool allows officers to make bids that require matched funding without full corporate assessment. This is useful where timescales are likely to be short. As with all capital projects, the revenue consequences of a bid need to be assessed.

1.52 As part of the decision to bid, senior officers will need to consider who is best placed to manage the bid, the resources and authority that they will need, and whether external consultancy advice should be sought. Such decisions will be partly practical and partly tactical. Authorities have resolved these issues in a number of ways. Over half the authorities that responded to the Phase 2 survey have employed consultants over the last three years to help with the bidding process and around half of London boroughs and metropolitan and unitary authorities have also appointed additional staff.

Presenting the bid

1.53 Colour printing, superior bindings, and so on, are unlikely to win on their own. But how the bid is presented is important. Of those authorities that have engaged consultants to help with the bid, two-thirds have used them to advise them on the presentation of bids. Where oral presentations are to be made, rehearsals and agreement on the role of those participating are vital.

Other issues

1.54 It is unlikely that everything will be right the first time, but approaching the task on a systematic basis will help (Box 1A). Some authorities arrange for the bids to be 'audited' by one or more officers with experience of bidding and who can suggest alterations and improvements to both presentation and content. If this is not possible, arranging for someone who is not involved in the bid to read it through critically will help. If the bid fails, authorities should find out why. Informal debriefing is given by funders. The bid may be re-submitted in the following round, building on the funders' perspective and the experience gained.

Box 1A
Bidding: a good practice checklist

Managing the bid	
How well prepared is the authority for submitting the bid?	
– Does the authority gather information about current and future bid-led funding?	
– Do elected members and officers know how projects are appraised by government offices?	
– Has the authority established communication links with funders to discuss issues and seek advice?	
– Do procedures and structures enable effective co-ordination of bids from different departments?	
– Has the authority drawn up and agreed a capital strategy?	
– Does the authority have a project bank so that it can react to calls for projects at short notice?	
– Do bids match corporate priorities?	
– Are there systematic procedures for tracking and managing the progress of each bid application?	
– Are there procedures for monitoring project implementation and management?	
– Are there procedures for identifying, at an early stage, projects which are underperforming and for which outputs may need to be renegotiated with the funder or corrective action taken?	
– Has matched funding been identified in the capital programme?	
Is the authority building successful partnerships?	
– Does the authority seek partners with common goals and objectives?	
– Has a framework for the partnership been agreed?	
– Are partnership arrangements set out in a legal agreement?	
– Have the roles and responsibilities of all partners (including the authority) been clarified and agreed?	
– Have the financial commitmments of all partners been agreed?	
– How effectively is the local community involved in the selection of projects?	
– Has the authority considered ways of pooling expertise with other local authorities, agencies and the private sector to share costs and skills?	
The bid document	
Is it well written?	
– Is it clearly linked to the competitive criteria?	
– Is it clearly laid out?	
– Does it follow the bidder's recommended format and length?	
– Is it in plain English?	
– Does it address the issues in a systematic way?	

– Is it short, to the point, with technical details consigned to appendices?	
– Does it have a clear coherent theme?	
– Is it in a uniform and consistent style?	
– Are graphics and tables used where they illustrate points more effectively than text?	
– Has it been proofread for basic errors?	
Does it address wider issues?	
– Does it include background information on the need for the bid?	
– Has the bid been agreed with partners?	
– Is it consistent with local, regional and national strategic plans?	
– Is it consistent with the funder's wider interests? (For example, how does it relate to ministers' statements; to the objectives of the funding body's corporate plan; or to professional bodies' approval of any innovative methods involved in the bid.)	

Presenting the bid

How well is the bid presented?	
– Has the bid presentation been rehearsed?	
– Is the length of the presentation appropriate?	
– Have the best presenters been selected?	
– Are graphics being used to best effect?	
– Does the authority need to seek advice on how to present the bid?	

Resourcing the bid

Has the bid been adequately resourced?	
– Does the authority have the right number of staff with appropriate skills to put together and manage the bid?	
– Is the work of staff co-ordinated?	
– Are there any skills which the authority needs to buy in?	
– How can staff skills be developed to match requirements?	

Checklist for action

Aspects of performance	Good practice features	Current practice	Action
Meeting needs	Assess needs and agree priorities.		
	Review proposed projects for compliance with the authority's needs and priorities.		
Knowing the property stock	Review property usage regularly.		
	Update full stock condition details regularly.		
	Use property database to prepare maintenance schedules and identify capital projects.		
Planning horizon	Use a planning horizon of three years or more.		
	Approve projects at key stages.		
Bidding effectively	Select projects which build partnerships with the private sector and other public sector organisations, and involve the community.		
	Work with the funder to clarify assessment criteria.		
	Make provision in the capital programme for matching funding.		
	Review the need for specialist staff and external support.		
	Review bids before they are submitted to the funder.		
Managing resources	Monitor total expenditure against budget, and actual commitments against planned commitments at least monthly.		
	Monitor milestone dates for all projects at least monthly.		
	Develop alternative projects that can be started at short notice when slippage occurs.		
	Minimise effects of annuality of funding by maintaining/ building up reserves.		
	Plan the use of professional services.		
	Avoid staffing for peaks.		
	Systematically review project and programme outcomes.		

2 Organisation Management

Successful projects require authorities to:

- adopt a management framework in which key roles and responsibilities are clearly defined and fulfilled;

- allocate and monitor human resources needed at each stage of a project; and

- set up systems that provide all concerned with clear and timely information.

The impact of capital controls, the increasing importance of bid-led funding and users' expectations are putting greater pressure on authorities to deliver projects to tight budgets and timetables, and to high quality standards. But many authorities could improve the delivery of their projects by giving more management attention to the allocation of roles and responsibilities and the effectiveness of communications between all those involved. This chapter considers these issues and makes the following recommendations.

Authorities should:	*This will have the following benefits:*
◆ define the roles and responsibilities of all involved	◆ greater role clarity and improved accountability
◆ plan and monitor human resources for each project to match availability to requirements	◆ better use of resources that are watched more closely to project needs; project delays minimised
◆ implement an organisational structure that is comprehensive and facilitates key tasks	◆ systematic approach to the management of projects ensures that all key aspects of a project are considered; the opportunity for error is minimised
◆ implement systems that generate appropriate, accurate and timely information	◆ better decisions that are based on sound information
◆ implement systems for communicating information	◆ project team members fulfil their roles more effectively
◆ have procedures for the completion and administrative closure of projects	◆ lessons learnt fed back to improve future performance; users given accurate information about maintenance and operation of services.

Roles and responsibilities

◆ How well do we define and allocate roles and responsibilities to each member of the project team?

◆ How well are people with key roles equipped to fulfil their responsibilities?

2.1 Many people must work together as team to ensure that projects are successful (Exhibit 2.1, overleaf). They will each have roles and responsibilities which must be defined clearly to avoid confusion and improve accountability (Box 2A, overleaf).

Exhibit 2.1
The team

Many people must work together to deliver
successful projects.

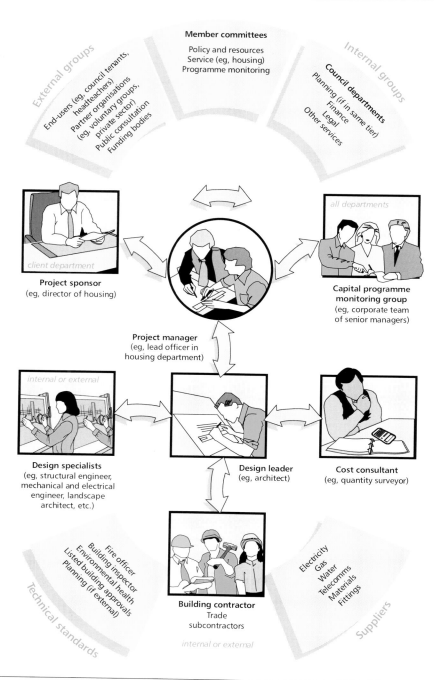

Member committees

Policy and resources
Service (eg, housing)
Programme monitoring

External groups

End-users (eg, council tenants,
headteachers)
Partner organisations
(eg, voluntary groups,
private sector)
Public consultation
Funding bodies

Internal groups

Council departments
Planning (if in same tier)
Finance
Legal
Other services

client department

Project sponsor
(eg, director of housing)

all departments

**Capital programme
monitoring group**
(eg, corporate team
of senior managers)

Project manager
(eg, lead officer in
housing department)

internal or external

Design specialists
(eg, structural engineer,
mechanical and electrical
engineer, landscape
architect, etc.)

Design leader
(eg, architect)

Cost consultant
(eg, quantity surveyor)

Technical standards

Fire officer
Building inspector
Environmental health
Listed building approvals
Planning (if external)

Building contractor
Trade
subcontractors

internal or external

Suppliers

Electricity
Gas
Water
Telecomms
Materials
Fittings

Source: Audit Commission survey

Box 2A
Roles and responsibilities of the project team

The team	Role	Responsibility
Client team		
Normally a service committee working through a relevant department – the client is responsible for procuring construction works, paying for them and owning the completed assets.	**Capital programme monitoring group** A corporate team of senior managers/directors	– reviews potential projects before they are recommended to members for inclusion in the capital programme; – monitors progress against the agreed capital programme; and – oversees the capital programme and reports to members on an exception basis.
	Project sponsor A senior person in the client department, often the director. The project sponsor should: – possess the skills to lead and manage the client role; – have the authority to take day-to-day decisions; and – have access to people who are making key decisions. The project sponsor can appoint a construction adviser (also referred to as the 'informed' or 'intelligent' client) who will provide professional advice. If the client department does not have the necessary skills in-house, an external consultant should be appointed. The construction adviser: – should understand the services provided by the client; but – should not have a vested interest in any of the options being considered.	– acts as focal point for key decisions about progress and variations; – decides on procurement strategy; – appoints design team; – carries out effective tendering process; – ensures good communications and teamwork; – appraises options in view of the client's objectives, including alternatives to construction; – develops a project strategy; and – estimates costs and assembles funding.
	Project manager Project managers can come from a variety of backgrounds but will need to have the competencies to co-ordinate and manage all aspects of a project from inception to completion. They must be able to work closely and effectively with all members of the team. The role may be fulfilled by a member of the client department or by an external appointment. In some circumstances the role may be combined with that of design team leader.	– agrees with the project sponsor the scope of the project, the quality of design, materials and construction, and the project budget; – develops a project plan which is agreed with the project sponsor; – identifies and acquires the skills and resources needed to deliver the project; – recommends most appropriate contracts for the project; – manages and controls the skills and resources used during the life of the project; – liaises/consults regularly with stakeholders, including users; – liaises regularly with the project sponsor and reports on major issues; – monitors delivery/expenditure; and – carries out post-project review.

The team	Role	Responsibility
Design team		
The technical nature of many projects means that professional advice will be required throughout. Advice is usually provided by the design team. Members of the team can be appointed separately or they may be part of a multi-disciplinary organisation. They have to work together as a design team to produce an integrated design. Whether they are in-house staff or external consultants, they should be selected on the basis of quality and price and not on price alone. The design team will include: – architects – surveyors – structural engineers – mechanical and electrical engineers – landscape architects.	**Design team leader** Usually an architect but may be an engineer or a surveyor. The team leader may be assisted by a clerk of works in supervising construction work.	– manages the work of the design team to ensure that it meets the needs of the clients and users, is within budget and to the agreed timescale; – ensures that sufficient time is given to briefing and design; – uses specialists when required; – develops detailed design within agreed timescale, cost and quality; – prepares bills of quantities and tender documents, including full working drawings; – reports regularly to project manager on progress; and – supervises operations on site.
	Design specialists These include structural engineers, mechanical and electrical engineers and landscape architects. Authorities which use in-house staff may not have the workload to employ full-time specialists.	– provide specialist advice to design team; – develop detailed specialist design within agreed timescale, cost and quality; and – supervise specialist operations on site.
	Cost consultant Usually a quantity surveyor. On small projects a separate appointment may not be justified and the role is taken on by the designer.	– advises the design team on cost aspects of the design; – prepares the cost plan; – prepares bills of quantities; and – negotiates on costs.
Construction team		
Usually appointed by competitive tendering but price should not be the sole factor in selecting a contractor. It may be either the authority's direct labour organisation or an external contractor supported by subcontractors.	**Building contractor and subcontractors** The main contractor will manage works on site to specification, time, cost and quality, supported by subcontractors who will provide specialist services.	– provide the project manager with a construction programme; – provide information to end-user; – make arrangements for working round existing occupiers; and – deliver construction programme.
Member committees		
	Policy and resources; service committees (for example, housing or education).	– identify service needs and set overall priorities; – review corporate procedures that test whether potential projects meet overall priorities and service needs; – approve overall tendering arrangements; – approve projects to proceed to detailed design and construction; – monitor project progress, particularly on an exception basis; – monitor programme progress at least twice a year; and – review programme to ensure that it meets service needs and that priorities are appropriate.

The team	Role	Responsibility
Other stakeholders		
A number of other stakeholders will have an interest in the outcome of a project. But unlike the client, the design team and the contractor, they are outside the direct control of the project manager. However, the project sponsor and the project manager should make arrangements to ensure that these stakeholders are consulted and that their views are fully taken into account.	**External groups – users** (for example, tenants, teachers) They have a stake in the end product. Users cannot always be readily identified (eg, in a town centre redevelopment users will be current and potential traders as well as shoppers/office workers) but the project sponsor, the project manager and the design team must make arrangements to consult potential users. The consultation process, if not well managed, could have an impact on costs and the timeliness of the project.	– to explain their needs and requirements so that they can be incorporated into a project brief; and – nominate a representative(s) for liaison during design and construction processes.
	External groups – partners (for example, voluntary groups, private sector) The extent of their roles and responsibilities will normally need to be clearly set out in a legal agreement.	– fulfil their responsibilities as set out in the legal agreement.
	Internal groups It is likely that almost all projects will need additional input from planning, finance and legal departments. The project manager should ensure that they are included in the project team and that their roles and responsibilities are communicated and are well understood. The roles and responsibilities should be included in a service level agreement between the 'other departments' and the project sponsor's department.	– provide appropriate support as and when required by the project manager and in accordance with the service level agreement.
	Technical standards Projects must comply with a number of statutory technical standards. The project manager needs to implement systems to ensure that the people who enforce them – fire officer, building inspector, environmental health officer and planning department (if external) – are consulted at the appropriate time and that their views are considered and taken into account.	– advise on statutory requirements which the project has to comply with; and – issue, where appropriate, certificates and other operational permits.
	Suppliers These include the utilities, and materials and fittings suppliers. (i) The responsibilities of the supplier of materials and fittings will be included in the contract between the authority and the supplier. Where specialist materials or fittings are used, the contract should set out how the supplier will: – provide appropriate information and support to the design team; and – ensure that the materials are used correctly. (ii) The utilities should be consulted at the design stage to identify potential restrictions on the design. The utilities must also be consulted on the project plan to ensure that they can provide their services as set out in the plan.	– provide technical and cost information on their products; and – supply services or materials to agreed specifications.

Empowerment

2.2 Defining the roles and responsibilities of members of the project team is an essential element in the delivery of successful projects. But they also have to be equipped to carry out their tasks. They must have delegated authority to take decisions; to take action; and to require others to take action. The extent of delegation should be clearly set out when roles are defined and responsibilities allocated. For example, the project manager should have the authority to approve changes to the project design, within defined cost parameters, without first seeking the prior approval of the project sponsor or the client committee. Similarly, once a project is approved to proceed to construction, the project manager and the project sponsor will have delegated authority to invite tenders; to evaluate them and award the contract.

2.3 Members of the project team must also have the skills to enable them to fulfil their roles. These skills are likely to be gained by relevant:

- education and training leading to a professional qualification;
- continuous professional development; and
- experience which is supported by a successful track record.

Human resources

- How effectively do we plan and deploy our human resources?
- How well do we monitor our human resources?

Planning

2.4 Project managers need to strike a balance: too little professional input is likely to increase the risk of poor design, increased costs and delays, but too much is expensive. An effective system for planning and managing the deployment of staff and consultants is therefore essential for the authority to ensure that each project is appropriately resourced. The demand on the system will depend on the scale and value of the authority's capital programme. However, it must be sufficiently robust to meet the timetable for each project and it should include mechanisms:

- to forecast resources required;
- to prioritise and allocate in-house resources; and
- to identify the need for external consultancy resources.

2.5 The level of resources required and the stage at which the different members of the team are employed will vary during the life of the project (Exhibit 2.2). But the level of activity will also vary. For instance, at the detailed design stage the design team's level of activity is high but it reduces during the construction period. Managers need up-to-date and accurate information to plan and allocate resources to projects so that skills and workloads are carefully matched. Some authorities use a paper-based approach to the planning and allocation of resources (Exhibit 2.3). Others use computer-based management information systems that enable them to plan and monitor a number of projects and to make adjustments as required. These systems will typically hold:

- details of project programmes – actual and planned;
- target predictions of resources required for each team member of a project;

Exhibit 2.2
Allocation of human resources for
projects designed and delivered
traditionally

The level of resources required varies
during the life of the project.

Source: Audit Commission

The team:					
Contractor					
Clerk of works					
Design team					
Design leader					
Project manager					
Construction adviser					
Project sponsor					
Project stages	Get started	Scope and approval	Detailed design	Construct	Complete and review

Exhibit 2.3
Project resources plan

Each project should have a resources plan so that skills and workloads are matched.

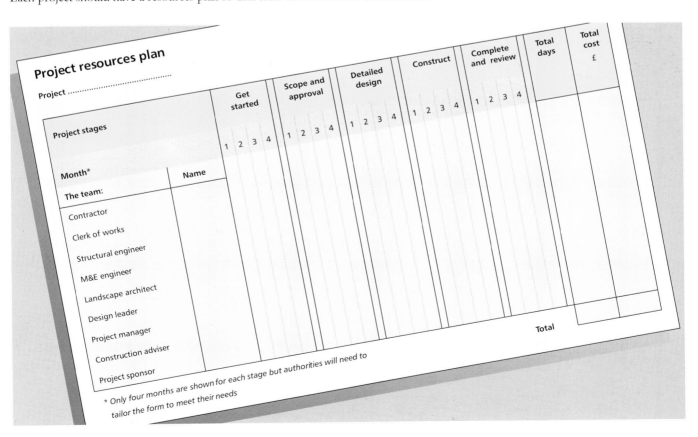

Source: Audit Commission

- records of actual time spent by each member of the team on each stage of the project; and
- hourly rates for each member of staff.

But the systems also provide essential information on:

- overall projections of people's availability in summary format;
- comparisons between time spent against targets, costs and time remaining; and
- time and cost reports for each member of staff against targets set.

Monitoring

2.6 Any construction project will be subject to pressures and constraints that will potentially require adjustment to its programme and/or human resources required in order to meet it. This makes it necessary for authorities to have in place systems to:

- monitor the staff resources available in relation to those required by the client, the design team and support services; and
- to manage the necessary changes in resource levels.

2.7 The complexity of the monitoring systems will depend on the size of the authority's capital programme as well as the extent of technical work that is carried out by external consultants. Authorities that rely almost entirely on external consultants must monitor the quality of their work (Chapter 8). But authorities which have an in-house technical function must also monitor how their staff are used. At Wirral Metropolitan Borough, for example, the property services department sets resource targets at the start of each project to establish the cost of fees and the time commitment of each member of the design team. These are reviewed and adjusted if necessary at each meeting of the design team. Managers receive regular reports which allow them to review:

- staff levels and work allocation;
- expenditure and project viability; and
- fee levels for similar work.

Organisational structure

- Do we have a comprehensive and well understood structure for each project that encourages effective teamwork?

2.8 Authorities organise themselves in a variety of ways to support capital projects. Many authorities retain an in-house technical capacity. This not only delivers a technical service, but is also responsible for some aspects of the client role, in particular acting as construction adviser. But there is no universal model of best practice: each has advantages and disadvantages (Exhibit 2.4). However, the key requirement is a comprehensive organisational structure in which roles are clearly defined and responsibilities allocated.

2.9 Many fieldwork authorities were well organised. But in a small number of projects, the service departments lacked the expertise to fulfil the client responsibilities, which were taken over by the design team. Where this occurred, the Audit Commission's fieldwork suggests that the service departments are more likely to lose ownership of projects, with the risk that end-users might not be satisfied with the outcome. This emphasises the need

Exhibit 2.4
Potential means of allocating responsibility for key roles in construction projects

Authorities organise themselves in different ways.

Role			Potential advantages	Potential disadvantages
Service provider (project sponsor/ project manager)	Construction adviser (informed/ intelligent client)	Technical service		
Service department incorporates technical section — Service department			- technical service more focused on task - better control by client department - easier communications	- no property overview - lack of consistency - control of resources more difficult - roles confused - technical services totally dependent on service department's workload
Property department provides technical section and acts as landlord for service departments — Service departments / Property department			- property overview - consistency across authority - maximises skills - better control of resources - greater opportunity to employ specialists	- insensitive to client's needs and priorities - 'manages' client role - roles confused
Core technical team acts as expert client for service providers – consultants provide technical services — Service departments / Core team / Consultants			- clarity of roles - all clients receive the same priority - flexibility - resources acquired when needed	- can create barriers to close working - loss of direct expertise - extended/difficult communications - no property overview
Technical services department provides assistance to service departments to fulfil their client role — Service departments / Technical department			- clarity of roles - maximises skills - control of resources - consistency across authority - communications	- 'manages' client role - insensitive to client's needs and priorities - no property overview

Source: Audit Commission

for the roles of the client and the design team to be clearly defined and performed by different people (see Box 2A, p35 – the role of the project sponsor).

2.10 The organisational arrangements should be specified for every project, although this might be done informally by the acceptance and application of standard procedures for routine projects. Arrangements for all other projects should be formally documented. But the organisational structure must be judged against the demands of each project:

◆ projects that are essentially straightforward and/or repetitive should be carried out within a framework of well-understood and documented standard procedures;

◆ complex, large or particularly important projects demand individual consideration of the project organisation and, if necessary, special arrangements. One approach used successfully by some authorities is to appoint a representative 'steering group' to be responsible for briefing and general oversight of the project. Projects where a number of parties have a client interest will require arrangements for the client role to be defined clearly; and

◆ joint ventures with bodies external to the authority require particular care and clarity; the arrangements should be underpinned by legal agreements.

2.11 Whatever approach an authority adopts, organisational arrangements for each project must be put in place in good time and reviewed as required.

2.12 The single most important feature of effective organisational arrangements is the ability of all involved to work as a *team*. This is as much the product of a culture of co-operation as of any set of formal procedures. Members and chief officers can play a key role in creating a culture where flexible, co-operative and cross-departmental working is the order of the day.

Communications

◆ How effective are our arrangements for communicating with all involved?

2.13 A brief, plans, estimates and reports are all part of the life of a construction project. A key task for all involved in them is to communicate effectively. For example:

◆ the design team must get from the client all necessary briefing information, and provide plans and other project details to the contractor; and

◆ the contractor needs to liaise with existing tenants/occupiers during construction and provide end-users with all essential information to enable them to run and maintain the completed project.

Effective communications do not evolve or happen by accident. They must be planned from the outset and they must be appropriate to each role in the project.

Communications planning

2.14 The key steps in planning project communications are:

◆ identifying the information needs of all participants in the project;

◆ putting in place the procedures to generate and communicate the information required (and only that information); and

◆ ensuring that the procedures take account of the requirements of the project programme.

2.15 The detail and rigour of the procedures should be planned to match the nature of the project. The more complex the project (in terms of the range of construction activities, the technology to be employed, the number of stakeholders, etc) the greater the need for formality and detail in communications management. For example, one fieldwork authority has a technical services department with a formal quality management system which is certified to ISO9000. The system ensures that projects are thoroughly documented. It also imposes a discipline on communications. In contrast, another fieldwork authority relies heavily on informal contacts between long-serving officers who are all located in one building.

2.16 The procedures for communicating effectively must also take into account the authority's structure – the greater the number of tasks carried out in separate or remote parts of the organisation, the more disciplined the procedures will need to be.

2.17 There are a number of communication tools that project teams can and should use. The choice of tool will depend on the stage of the project, what is communicated and to whom (Box 2B). However, a culture of teamwork will again be the essential lubricant in the communications machinery. While this cannot be replaced entirely by formal systems, in practice it can overcome shortcomings in procedures. On the other hand, a lack of teamwork will undermine the effectiveness of well-structured systems.

Box 2B
Applying communication tools to
construction projects

Means of communication	Key questions	Stage of the project
Team meetings	– Who should attend? – How often should they be held? – How should follow-up action be pursued?	– All stages
Site meetings	– How often are they needed? – Who should be involved? – How should decisions be: – recorded? – appropriately authorised? – followed up?	– Design – Planning – Construction
Workshops	– Who needs to be involved? – Are external facilitators needed? – How are conclusions to be recorded?	– Brief – Design (including value-management discussions) – Post-contract award – Post-project review
Briefings	– Is their purpose clear? – Who should attend? – Are supporting handouts required?	– Invitation to tender – Handover
Drawings	– Are they clear to non-specialists? – Are they accurate? – Are they up to date?	– Design – Pre-tender – Handover
Models (including show flats)	– Are they needed to aid design discussions and development? – How much will they cost?	– Design
Computer-aided design (CAD)	– How can CAD be used to help end-users influence the design?	– Design
E-mail and memos	– Who should receive them? – Does a copy need to be filed for future reference?	– All stages
Bulletins	– Who needs to receive them? – What information should they contain? – How often should they be produced?	– All stages

Source: Audit Commission

Completion and administrative closure

◆ How satisfactory are our arrangements for bringing projects to a close?

2.18 It is all too easy to overlook the final phase of a project. Completion of construction, handover and tying up the loose ends is often not well managed. Completion and handover should work smoothly if they have been built into earlier phases of the project (Box 2C).

2.19 Effective information will also help to draw a project to a close successfully. A construction project can generate a large volume of information that should be filed for future reference to resolve any contractual disputes. A sound record of events is essential to establish a reasonable settlement. But records are also essential when carrying out a post-project review. A clear perspective both of good and bad results is essential to feed back lessons for future projects.

2.20 Following agreement of the final account, information should be archived in a suitable format, indicating contents and time limit. Retention of key data relating to time, cost and other parameters in an accessible file will enable the authority:

◆ to build a portfolio of historical information;

◆ to benchmark its performance internally and potentially externally; and

◆ to establish a policy of continuous improvement (see Chapter 8).

Box 2C
Good practice checklist for
the completion and handover
of projects

Planning for completion	
When to start?	Planning for completion should start as soon as the decision is made to go ahead with the project. During the briefing and design stages, decisions about materials and equipment should take into account the maintenance, servicing, and day-to-day management requirements of the finished project.
Preparing for occupation	The occupation/use of the completed project should be planned from the outset. The following matters need to be considered: – will the building need to be fitted out? – will it need staff to manage it? – what costs should be included in the revenue budget? – who is responsible for allocating space and the moving arrangements? – what arrangements need to be made to move people?
Commissioning	Discussions about the equipment to be managed should take place during the design stage. Arrangements should be made for the contractor to test equipment and demonstrate how it operates before handover takes place.
Handover	
Practical completion	The client takes over responsibility for the security, maintenance and insurance of the project. The builder is responsible for making good any defects that arise during the defects liability period.
Arrangements to be made	The client needs to make arrangements for: – recording and reporting defects; – maintaining and servicing equipment; – insurance; – compliance with statutory regulations; and – to keep records such as as-built drawings and operating instructions.

Checklist for action

Aspects of performance	Good practice features	Current practice	Action
Roles and responsibilities	Clearly define and allocate roles and responsibilities.		
	Train people with key roles and give them authority to fulfil responsibilities.		
Planning and monitoring human resources	Systems to forecast resources required; prioritise and allocate in-house resources; and identify need for external consultancy		
	Identify clearly the roles and responsibilities of in-house technical staff.		
	Monitor the deployment of human resources against set targets and change as necessary.		
Organisational structure	Define client role clearly.		
	Document formally arrangements for managing projects from inception to completion.		
	Underpin joint ventures with legal agreement.		
	Document special arrangements for complex, large or important projects.		
	Effective teamwork.		
Information	Identify information needs of all participants in projects.		
	Put in place formal procedures to generate and communicate the information required (and only that required) by participants in projects.		
	Client manages the involvement and contributions of all stakeholders in the project, and minimises delays and costs.		
	Client provides the design team with clear, complete and timely briefs.		
	Design team provides tenderers/contractor with completed drawings and other essential project information on time.		
	Include the contractor's requirement to communicate with tenants/occupiers/other stakeholders in the contract document.		
Completion and closure	Hand over project details, such as drawings and manuals, to the client for future reference.		
	Give users demonstrations and instructions by both the contractor and the design team.		

A project will represent good value for money if:

- it is approved within the context of a corporate framework in which needs and priorities are assessed, resources are identified, and service plans are met;

- it is the most effective option for achieving the client's objectives;

- a comprehensive brief is discussed with the client and signed off before detailed design work begins; and

- unavoidable changes during design are managed.

3 Option and Design Management

Many authorities have procedures to enable them to identify potential projects in a systematic manner and to consult users before briefs are drawn up. But authorities could tighten up their procedures, consider the most effective means of achieving project objectives and ensure that projects are constructed as cost-effectively as possible. This chapter considers these issues and makes the following recommendations.

Authorities should:	*This will have the following benefits:*
◆ have procedures for identifying and justifying projects in a disciplined manner within a corporate framework	◆ only projects which meet overall priorities, are based on users' needs and support service plans are included in the capital programme
◆ authorise projects at defined stages	◆ projects are reviewed to assess whether they are still justified particularly if the scope is not clearly defined at inception, they are large or complex, or funding is uncertain
◆ ensure project briefs reflect users' needs and are signed off by the client before detailed design work starts	◆ projects will meet users' requirements and avoid late changes which have cost, time and quality implications
◆ have procedures for managing responses to change in the scope of a project arising during design	◆ best option selected to maintain quality and minimise the risk of cost and time overruns
◆ appraise different options for delivering project objectives	◆ most cost-effective option selected

Making time to plan

◆ How well do we plan and design our projects?

3.1 The maxim 'act in haste – repent at leisure' is particularly relevant to capital projects. Lack of time for planning and rushed design give rise to poor user satisfaction, increased project costs, delays and generally lower quality. For example, one authority wanted to convert a property into a social services day centre. The time available to complete the project was compressed into a financial year by the funding deadlines imposed by the Department of Health. The rushed nature of the design process meant that standards had to be reduced. This is likely to result in higher maintenance costs. In addition, completion was delayed and the authority had to meet increased construction costs from its own resources.

3.2 With time-limited funding, there can be a particular pressure to rush, even if the time-limited funding is only a small proportion of total funding. Authorities can lose more by trying to achieve a deadline to acquire time-limited funds than by finding alternative sources of funding for well-planned projects. Detailed planning should always begin as early as possible because the potential for cost reduction (and for avoiding costly mistakes) is greatest at the start of a project (Exhibit 3.1).

Exhibit 3.1
Opportunity to influence costs

Late changes increase costs.

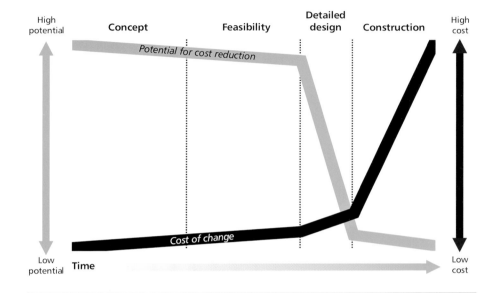

Source: Audit Commission

3.3 A well-planned and designed project has to satisfy a number of criteria. It must meet needs; it has to be justified; and it must be clearly specified and cost-effectively designed.

Meeting needs

◆ Do our projects relate to our service delivery strategy?

◆ Are our projects the most cost-effective way of meeting current needs?

3.4 The purpose of a project is to meet service needs, and expenditure is justified only if it does so. Service needs should be assessed (Chapter 1), and options for meeting them evaluated as part of the project development process. Authorities should also be sure that a project relates to their service delivery strategy. For example, to meet the needs of elderly people an authority may decide to:

◆ provide domiciliary care through its own staff;

◆ provide daycare in its own buildings, using its own staff, vehicles and equipment to deliver care;

◆ provide residential care through its own staff in buildings that it has acquired or built; or

◆ enable others to provide such services – for example, through contracts or other involvement with the private and voluntary sectors.

The balance and exact form of service delivery will vary from one authority to another, but it is important that all projects are justified in terms of the agreed service plan.

Case Study 3.1
Devon County Council, Ivybridge
Community College

Addressing users' needs early on will
minimise changes during detailed
design and construction.

The authority set up a steering group. The group carried out a thorough analysis of:

◆ general population and curriculum trends; and

◆ the condition and suitability of existing buildings.

The group went on to develop the project brief, including identifying options regarding standards and phasing, with reference to likely funding. The group concentrated initially on getting basic accommodation right and then went into detailed considerations, including how the college would operate during construction. One result was very limited need for scope changes during design and construction.

Heads of department were involved in the briefing process and signed off the designs.

3.5 It is also important that authorities select projects on the basis of a full understanding of users' needs and that they are not working to outdated data or outmoded service delivery assumptions (Case Study 3.1). Census data, surveys, focus groups, feedback from front-line staff, study of best practice and service trends will all help authorities to identify accurately users' needs.

3.6 When a project has been selected and included in the capital programme it is locked into a process which will ultimately deliver a completed building or facility. This in itself can mean that alternatives, which may provide better value for money, are never explored. Value management (VM) can help authorities explore alternative solutions.

Value management

3.7 Value management is concerned with clarifying the aims and objectives of a project and how they can best be achieved (Ref. 7). It is particularly relevant to the earlier stages of the project, when scope and outline are being fixed (Exhibit 3.2). VM provides an opportunity to raise fundamental questions such as: Do we need to build at all? Do we have to build as much? Can we meet needs differently? But VM can also help challenge the assumptions that are built into the project brief as it is developed. VM is characterised by workshop meetings, involving the client and the design team, that are held at key stages of the project and are led by an experienced facilitator. It is at these workshops that the concept and design development are critically evaluated to test whether objectives are being met and to find ways of improving value.

3.8 Fieldwork authorities had limited awareness of VM. Nonetheless, some had informally applied some of the principles of VM to their capital programmes in challenging both generally accepted objectives and traditional means of achieving them, and in adopting new strategies to achieve best value (Case Studies 3.2 and 3.3 [overleaf]). Only one authority had formalised its approach (Case Study 3.4, overleaf). In the private sector, VM has produced impressive results. So much so that at BAA plc, VM is applied to all projects with a value above £250,000.

'VM provides an opportunity to raise fundamental questions such as: Do we need to build at all? Do we have to build as much? Can we meet needs differently?'

Exhibit 3.2
Application of value management

Proposed projects are systematically reviewed to ensure that they meet needs.

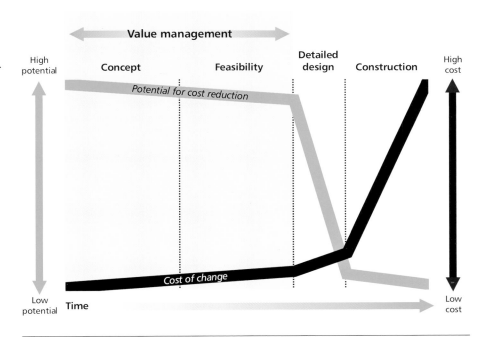

Source: Audit Commission

Case Study 3.2
Doncaster Metropolitan Borough Council housing refurbishment programme

Following the review of refurbishment costs, a decision was taken to do less, to consider maintenance costs and meet tenants' needs.

Traditionally, Doncaster MBC refurbished its housing stock to a very high standard, spending about £50,000 per dwelling. This practice was questioned because the sum was greater than:

◆ the value of the dwelling, and much greater that the sum it would fetch under 'right to buy'; and

◆ the cost of a new dwelling, which could be built for less.

The current policy is to target spending on key objectives:

◆ cavity wall insulation, for energy efficiency;

◆ UPVC doors and windows, for reduced maintenance costs; and

◆ refurbishing kitchens and bathrooms, to satisfy tenant aspirations.

There is now a ceiling on refurbishment costs of £25,000 per dwelling.

Case Study 3.3
Newark and Sherwood District
Council housing modernisation

Strong tenant feedback resulted in a
change of priorities.

Up to the early 1980s, Newark and Sherwood DC undertook 'traditional' modernisations of its housing stock – new windows/kitchen/bathrooms/background heating. However, strong tenant feedback caused the council to rethink and to identify as its priorities:

- the eradication of condensation; and
- 'affordable warmth'.

The Council adopted an energy strategy to meet these objectives, in which available resources were targeted on successive district-wide measures that achieved the greatest benefit for the greatest number in the shortest time. These measures included:

- roof insulation;
- cavity fill; and
- high-efficiency boilers in dwellings that could not be economically insulated.

Case Study 3.4
Improving value on an education
project

Value management techniques can help
result in savings of up to 25 per cent.

West Sussex County Council achieved a significant cost reduction by critically appraising the initial proposals; in particular, by:

- examining alternative uses for existing accommodation in conjunction with related needs for additional space;
- comparing the cost of options for adaptation/new-build against benefits achieved (structural alterations and/or modifications to building services were major cost factors); and
- consolidating new-build largely into one extension with a simple link to existing accommodation.

The authority reckoned that a saving of 25 per cent was achieved on the estimated cost of the initial scheme (£676,000).

Project justification

- How well do we justify projects?

3.9 A project must be justified in terms of the objectives that it is intended to achieve. Objectives should be clearly defined, endorsed by the client and consistent with the authority's overall policy objectives. VM may help to achieve clarity and consensus.

3.10 Defining objectives will provide the basis for appraising the project against its objectives and assessing it against other available options (Ref. 8). The rigour and formality of this process will depend on the nature of the project, but proposals should be backed by formal, documented option appraisals that take account of:

- efficiency in achieving objectives;
- timescales;
- funding availability/constraints;
- external/political constraints; and
- overall costs/benefits.

3.11 Options should not be constrained artificially by unwarranted assumptions, and might typically include:

- refurbishment of existing assets;
- new-build;
- 'no-build', that is, adoption of other expedients to achieve the ultimate objectives; and even
- 'do nothing'.

3.12 Project justification should be expressed in a 'business case' which is approved prior to significant expenditure on the project, demonstrating that the investment is justified by the anticipated benefits. The formality and depth of the statement justifying the project will depend on the nature of the project. A checklist formalises the approach and ensures that all issues are addressed (Case Study 3.5).

Case Study 3.5
Essex County Council's project justification

The process ensures that only projects that meet needs are included in the capital programme.

Before members agree to include projects in the capital programme, these have to be justified. These are reviewed by the Capital Programme Study Group and Management Team – a group of senior officers – and evaluated against criteria agreed by members.

The information that is collected and documented includes:
- the name of the responsible committee and the proposed start date;
- the name of the person responsible for overseeing the project in the client department;
- the purpose of the project and need;
- whether other options were considered and reasons for deciding to build;
- how the proposals relate to service requirements and to the authority's objectives;
- the results of the feasibility study undertaken or the reasons why it is not required;
- the results of the financial appraisal of the project;
- whether the project requires premises or land and when they will be required or available;
- whether planning permission is required;
- whether the project is to be carried out in partnership with other agencies such as another local authority or health authority;
- the capital costs; and
- the revenue implications.

Clear specification

- How clear are project briefs?
- Are briefs signed off by project sponsors?

3.13 The project brief is the cornerstone of a successful project, since it should be based on a detailed analysis of the needs of the end-users of the project. The brief must establish the essential and desirable outcomes of the project so that they can be agreed and signed off by the project sponsor, the users and the project manager before detailed design is started. However, circumstances may arise that could result in changes during the detailed design or construction stages of a project. Authorities should anticipate change and attendant risks (Chapter 7) and implement procedures to minimise their impact. These procedures should define clearly who is responsible for identifying the changes, assessing their impact and taking action.

3.14 Fieldwork authorities recognised the importance of sound briefing, together with the need to involve all the project stakeholders (Chapter 2). They generally worked hard to ensure that the briefs clearly identified the needs that the projects were fulfilling. However, in some cases fieldwork authorities had devolved responsibility for developing the brief almost entirely to the design team. This is not the best approach. Although the outcome can be satisfactory where there is effective communication within the authority and with users, there were problems in one-quarter of the projects reviewed by the Audit Commission. Needs were not fully met because there was either confusion about who the real client was, or a failure of the various members of the project team (client departments, users, designers, contractors) to understand what was required or would be delivered.

Cost-effective design

- Are we cost effective?

3.15 It is essential that users, the project manager and the programme managers are all consulted about, and approve, the design of each project, since it is the design which most influences costs and success in meeting needs. Even though a design has been agreed, there is scope to improve value for money by removing unnecessary cost and adding client benefits or to improve quality by using value engineering (VE) techniques.

Value engineering

3.16 Value engineering, sometimes confused with value management, is a more restricted process which focuses upon individual components or materials to examine the appropriateness of the level of specification and associated costs (Exhibit 3.3). The basic assumption of VE is that there is always some unnecessary cost in a design which may arise from:

- an unnecessary component, fulfilling no useful function;
- the use of an unnecessarily expensive material;
- poor buildability; and
- higher lifecycle costs, arising from expensive maintenance, energy or operational requirements.

3.17 None of the fieldwork authorities had used VE to improve the cost-effectiveness of their designs. This finding was disappointing, as in the private sector it has produced impressive results (Case Study 3.6). In addition, the Highways Agency is now applying VE techniques to major road projects.

Exhibit 3.3
Application of value engineering

Designs are systematically reviewed to ensure that they are cost effective.

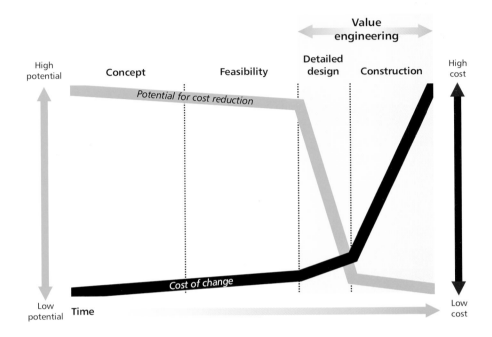

Source: Audit Commission

Case Study 3.6
Value engineering in the private sector

Value engineering can produce impressive results.

British Airports Authority plc (BAA) worked with its project manager and subcontractors to use VE to reduce the project cost and completion time for a canopy over its proposed visitor centre at Gatwick's South Tower.

BAA initially proposed a 100m long, 14m wide, barrel-vaulted rooflight to form an atrium for the visitor centre. When completed with double-glazed curved glass, as specified, the roofing contractor, Coxdrome, estimated the cost at £650,000.

Mace, a project management firm that works regularly with BAA, was asked to produce a feasibility study for the visitor centre. Mace asked its trade subcontractors to come up with ideas for cost savings and arranged a design workshop with BAA's designers to discuss alternative solutions. The original design required bespoke materials and structural steel support, but Coxdrome were able to offer two cheaper solutions that required less sophisticated 'engineering'.

Balancing cost against design, BAA rejected the cheapest alternative for aesthetic reasons, but accepted the second at a cost of £420,000 – a saving of 35 per cent. By working closely with Coxdrome and using standardised panels, the timetable for procuring the roof was reduced from 33 to 18 weeks.

Reproduced from Building, *8 March 1996.*

Checklist for action

Aspects of performance	Good practice features	Current practice	Action
Meeting needs	Make time for planning.		
	Base needs assessment on current data and evidence		
	Appraise projects systematically before including them in the capital programme.		
	Project briefs should be clear and signed off by all stakeholders.		
	Anticipate risks and implement procedures to minimise their impact.		
	Have procedures for managing change during design.		
Value for money	Implement value management and value engineering techniques.		

Effective procurement
management requires authorities
to:

- evaluate and select the most
  appropriate procurement
  approach for the project;

- identify all the services required;

- identify potential suppliers who
  are able to deliver to time and
  quality at a competitive price;
  and

- obtain services in the most
  effective manner from the
  suppliers which offer the best
  value.

4 Procurement Management

Most authorities do not adopt an explicit procurement strategy. They tend to rely on a traditional approach which often works well, but not always. They do this because they are familiar with it and may not have the relevant skills to manage unfamiliar types of contracts.

Authorities need to have a procurement strategy but they must also implement sound tendering procedures. Over half the projects reviewed had tendering periods which were less than the National Joint Consultative Committee for Building (NJCC)[1] norm of four weeks.

The Latham Report on the construction industry said that better relationships must replace the traditional antagonism between clients and contractors if better value for money is to be achieved in construction (Ref. 2). If authorities adopt an approach akin to that advocated by Latham, they will need to work more closely with professionals and contractors, and develop different ways of managing their relationships while still maintaining high standards of probity.

These issues are considered in this chapter and the following recommendations are made.

Authorities should:	**This will have the following benefits:**
◆ systematically evaluate and select the most appropriate procurement approach, on a project-by-project basis, having regard to the complexity of the project; the importance of design; timescale; the need for certainty of final cost and the allocation of risk	◆ the option selected provides best value for money
◆ consider how work is best phased or packaged	◆ the most cost-effective size of contract is chosen in the anticipated tender market
◆ review tendering procedures in line with good practice	◆ the choice of contractor is made in the most cost-effective manner
◆ appoint consultants on the basis of quality and price in line with good practice	◆ better quality projects
◆ develop a partnership approach to working with construction contractors, but at the same time maintain high standards of probity and define the role of internal audit	◆ contractors develop better understanding of authorities' requirements, resulting in improved value for money while maintaining high standards of probity

[1]
The NJCC has been formally wound up. The Construction Industry Board will be publishing good practice guidance on tendering periods.

58

Procurement strategy

- Do we systematically select the most appropriate procurement system for each project?
- Do we package/phase construction work to meet the needs of clients and users and to obtain best value?

4.1 A key part of planning any project is to consider the best method for procuring the goods and services required for its delivery. In particular, a construction project will require:

- technical services for surveys, design, cost consultancy and other essential construction advice; and
- construction services for the supply of materials and components, and to carry out construction work on site.

4.2 Effective procurement management requires a strategy for the procurement of both technical and construction services, and its implementation, so that:

- all the services required for the project are identified;
- potential suppliers who are able to deliver in time, to the required quality and at a competitive price are identified; and
- each service is obtained in the most effective way from the supplier offering the best value.

These principles will apply whether the services are provided in-house or obtained externally.

4.3 A procurement strategy should enable authorities to:

- consider systematically the most appropriate procurement system for each project; and
- how construction work should be phased/packaged to meet the needs of clients and users and to obtain best value.

Procurement system

4.4 The choice of building procurement systems varies widely, but can be grouped under three main categories:

- *Traditional contracting* – the client employs a number of organisations that are responsible separately for the design and the construction of the works;
- *Design and build* – one organisation (normally a contractor) assumes single point responsibility for both design and construction of the works; and
- *Construction management* – an organisation manages the construction process for a fee, with the construction work undertaken in separately tendered packages by works or trade contractors.

In practice, a range of detailed approaches exists within each of these categories, and the distinction between them is not rigid. Moreover, each approach has its advantages and disadvantages (Box 4A, overleaf).

Box 4A
Options for procurement

Procurement route		Key features	Basis of payment to the contractor
Traditional procurement	*The majority of construction projects undertaken by authorities are procured on a traditional basis. The approach frequently works well, but should not be considered an automatic choice, particularly for projects that are large, complex, or need to be completed quickly.*	○ the client appoints and briefs the design team. The design team designs the works and provides cost advice; ○ the design team leader acts as the client's principal adviser and agent; ○ the design team provides design and other documentation as a basis for tenders for the construction works; and ○ the client engages a contractor to construct the works to the design team's design. Although the contract for construction is between client and contractor, all instructions to and communications with the contractor is through a 'contract administrator' (normally the design team leader), who has to act impartially between client and contractor.	Payment methods carry different risks for the client: ○ **lump sum** – the contractor is awarded a contract for a stated sum based on a full description of the work to be carried out. Variations are usually possible, with adjustment to the contract sum. Lump-sum tendering is appropriate only if construction work is fully designed and described, and there are no major changes during construction; ○ **measured** – the contractor prices the work on quantities that are subject to remeasurement. This arrangement is used where the full scope of the work cannot be established until work is in progress; and ○ **cost reimbursement** – the contractor is paid the cost of labour, materials and equipment, together with a quoted fee for management costs and profit. Because of the inherent uncertainties, this arrangement is used only when other options are not available because of an overriding need for speed or the nature of the work.
Design and build	*Authorities use design and build less frequently than the traditional procurement approach. Design and build has been used successfully on relatively straightforward schemes.*	Under design and build, the client enjoys single-point responsibility for both design and construction. There are two main approaches that give the client varying degrees of influence over the design process: ○ **contractor's total design** – in which the contractor is responsible for the entire process of design from the point of taking the clients' brief. The approach places heavy demands on the client in defining project requirements. The client may require independent technical help to develop the brief and provide cost advice; and ○ **develop and construct** – where the client employs a 'scope design team' to take the project to scheme design stage and give cost advice. The contractor tenders on the basis of the scheme design, but is responsible for completing the design and every aspect of the process thereafter.	Subject to contractual arrangements for changes in client requirements, the contractor is paid the sum tendered to the client.
Construction management	*Although none of the fieldwork authorities use this procurement route, some have adopted an approach with similar characteristics – they divide construction work into packages, appoint trade contractors, manage them and co-ordinate them.*	○ a 'construction manager' is appointed at an early stage to manage the construction process for a fee; ○ the construction manager does not undertake any construction work. This is divided into packages, tendered and carried out by trade contractors, each having a contract with the client; ○ members of the design team are appointed by the client, as in the traditional system; and ○ the construction manager arranges and co-ordinates the trade contracts, and may also have responsibility for co-ordinating the design process. However, the construction manager is not responsible for the performance of the design team or individual trade contractors.	Subject to contractual arrangements but as advised by the construction manager.

Potential advantages	Potential disadvantages	Suitable for	Responsibility/risk

• the client can maintain a close relationship with the design team, important if detail design is critical;
• commitment to major expenditure (under the construction contract) does not come until the design is well developed and good clarity of final construction cost is possible; and
• it is widely familiar and understood, and frequently works well on smaller, simpler projects.
	• the sequential process of design development, tendering and construction cannot be readily compressed or overlapped;
	• separate responsibilities for design and construction can too easily:
	  – inhibit the potential contribution of the contractor to the design, particularly in relation to 'buildability'; and
	  – hinder teamwork, and contribute to confrontation and dispute over responsibilities.
	• it is often difficult to integrate the design contribution of specialist suppliers and installers; and
	• its track record is not good on large and complex schemes, or when design and measurement are not completed as required in readiness for tender.
		Most sizes of projects from very small to large.	Responsibilities are clear and risk reasonably shared.

• a single, clear point of responsibility; • transfer of design risk; • potential savings of time and cost through the integration and overlap of design and construction; and • clarity of final cost at an early stage.	• commercial pressures on the contractor are liable to lead to compromise in quality, particularly in design; • design standards may be difficult to define in the first instance, leading to disappointment or dispute; and • late changes in the brief are likely to be difficult and expensive to implement, if the client was unable to deliver a complete and clear statement of requirements prior to tendering.	**Develop and construct** may be used for medium/large projects where the client wants to control the design. **Contractor's total design** may be used for medium/large projects where the client wants responsibility in one place.	**Develop and construct** – responsibility lies with the design and build organisation after the design stage. **Contractor's total design** – design and build organisation takes most of the risk and responsibility.
• an opportunity to reduce overall timescales by overlapping design and construction; • a strong management framework able to deal with complex or difficult projects; and • some flexibility for change where work packages have not been tendered.	• construction management can increase the client's exposure to risk; • the final cost is subject to a greater uncertainty when construction begins than with traditional or design and build approaches; and • the client occupies a central position, with direct contractual relationships with the construction manager and each of the trade contractors. This demands a high level of skill and commitment, although the extent of involvement will depend on the degree of delegation to the construction manager.	Really suitable only for large or complex projects, with experienced clients.	The client keeps a high level of risk and responsibility. However, the client maintains control.

'Traditional contracting, which is the procurement route most familiar to authorities, should not be an automatic choice.'

4.5 Fieldwork authorities tended to be conservative in their choice of procurement system. They followed traditional approaches that used a limited number of standard forms of contract such as JCT80 or MW80 for building work and ICE 5th/6th edition for civil engineering work (standard forms of contract are described in Appendix 4). These forms of contract have the significant advantage of being familiar to authorities, design teams and local contractors. In some cases fieldwork authorities made them work well by completing designs before tendering, managing the tendering process effectively and establishing a teamwork approach.

4.6 Traditional contracting, which is the procurement route most familiar to authorities, should not be an automatic choice. Authorities should select systematically the procurement system most suited to the project or package of projects (Exhibit 4.1).

Packaging/phasing construction work

4.7 The packaging of construction works into one or more contracts is relatively simple for small or straightforward projects, but should always be carefully considered. For example, in a project to replace windows and roofs on a housing estate, the authority should consider:

◆ the optimum size of contract that will give the most economic pricing in the anticipated tender market;

◆ peripheral items such as minor repairs or redecoration that could be included cost effectively; and

◆ whether different elements should be renewed by different contractors with appropriate specialisms, or in a single contract.

Exhibit 4.1
Matching priorities and procurement systems

Authorities should select the system most suited to the project.

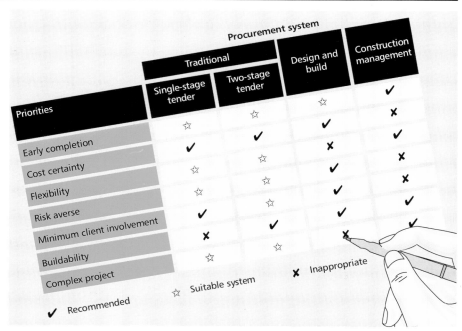

Source: Audit Commission adaptation of Davis Langdon Consultancy table

4.8 In large or complex projects, further consideration might include the need for or benefit to be achieved by:

♦ saving programme time by placing preliminary contracts, say for demolition;

♦ reducing risk by placing preliminary contracts to deal with known or suspected hazards, such as the identification and removal of asbestos or opening up to reveal defects in existing structures;

♦ meeting user or other needs by phasing or partial handovers of the principal contract, for which the tender and contract documents should specify access arrangements, commissioning and operation of services and insurances; and

♦ enabling continued use of existing sites by phasing the works into distinct packages which are undertaken in sequence.

4.9 The Commission's survey suggests that some authorities are not packaging or phasing construction work with a view to getting best value. On the other hand, fieldwork has also shown that some authorities have adopted good practice by considering carefully how they can best package/phase works to reflect their own priorities and needs, and also achieve the best response from local contractors (Case Studies 4.1 and 4.2 [overleaf]). A systematic approach will help authorities to decide on an appropriate packaging strategy (Box 4B, overleaf).

Case Study 4.1
Newark and Sherwood District Council energy efficiency programme

Packaging of works into contracts can optimise the benefits to the council and local contractors.

Newark and Sherwood DC needed to undertake a range of energy efficiency measures to improve its housing stock. In order to decide precisely how to set about this task, the authority considered:

♦ the types of work to be undertaken;

♦ the number and skills of contractors available to do the work;

♦ the timescales; and

♦ advice from contractors on the optimum size and value of work packages to achieve economy and continuity, in the context of the authority's requirements.

Work to meet these requirements was then packaged into a series of contracts that optimised the benefits to both the council and contractors, thus achieving highly competitive results. The packages ranged from cavity fill for 250 dwellings using a relatively large contractor, to much smaller contracts for boiler replacements using smaller local contractors.

Case Study 4.2
Lancaster City Council housing
refurbishment

Phasing of works can meet the needs of
the client and attract keen prices and the
right calibre of contractor.

In 1987 the council decided to refurbish 77 houses which had been built in 1946. The
properties needed to be vacant for the work to be carried out. As the properties were
in isolated rural areas, the relocation of tenants into alternative accommodation was
not feasible. To minimise the disruption to tenants, the authority bought mobile
homes which were then located near the properties that were being refurbished. The
mobile homes were transported to the different sites as contracts were let.

The authority examined various options for packaging the work and decided that
carrying out the refurbishment in a series of four/five contracts would provide the
optimum solution. This approach would also provide reasonable projects that would
attract keen prices and the right calibre of contractor.

In the event, the refurbishment of all 77 properties was successfully carried out in five
contracts, mostly of similar size, over a period of five years. The work, which was
tendered competitively for each contract, was carried out by the same contractor. The
design team took advantage of this situation to learn and develop, with the
contractor, the best approach to successive phases.

Box 4B
Packaging/phasing construction
work

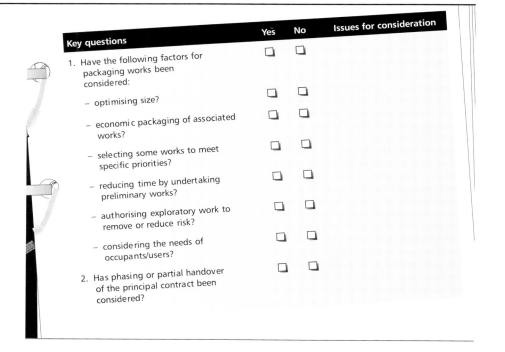

Procurement of technical services

♦ How effectively do we plan for technical and other professional services at project inception?

♦ Do we consider both quality and price when we select and appoint consultants?

4.10 The need for technical services and other professional skills will depend on the type and complexity of each project. For example:

♦ designing new-buildings or major alterations to an existing building will normally require the services of an architect;

♦ structural engineers will be required on all projects where structural performance requires specialist expertise;

♦ refurbishing an old building might best be undertaken by a building surveyor; and

♦ technically straightforward and repetitive projects can reasonably be taken on by a technician with architectural or surveying skills.

Legal advice may also be required if unusual arrangements are envisaged (for example, if amendments are made to a standard form of contract or if a project is sponsored in partnership with external bodies). For many projects the Construction (Design and Management) Regulations 1994 (Appendix 3) impose a duty on clients to appoint a competent 'planning supervisor' to co-ordinate health and safety matters during the design stage.

4.11 The procurement system that is chosen will also have an impact on the technical services and professional skills required. For example, the need for technical services on a design and build project will be limited to helping the client prepare the project brief and tender documents, and to act as the client's representative during construction. While in a traditional procurement approach additional skills are required to design the project and to administer the contract.

4.12 Whatever the complexity of the project or the procurement system chosen, it is important that the need for technical and other professional services is assessed at inception and plans made for their provision (Chapter 2).

4.13 Many authorities have in-house technical services to cover the base workload (Chapter 1). They engage external consultants if the project demands particular technical skills that are not available in-house or where the authority's technical resources are committed on other projects. A few authorities rely almost entirely on external consultants for technical services.

Selection and appointment of consultants

4.14 In selecting and managing members of the design team authorities need to balance quality and price. But fieldwork authorities generally appointed consultants who submitted the lowest bids. Anecdotal evidence suggests that this practice may have led to unnecessarily heavy designs and/or poor service. On the other hand, there were examples of authorities making it a clear objective to appoint the right people for the job (Case Study 4.3, overleaf). These examples are in line with recommended good practice in the construction industry (Refs. 9 and 10).

Case Study 4.3
Appointment of consultants by the
London Borough of Greenwich

A thorough selection process is more
likely to result in the appointment of
appropriate consultants and a successful
project outcome.

The authority appointed private architects on a £5 million estate action project to reclad and improve a tower block. The consultant selection process was thorough and included:

- ◆ drawing up an outline brief for the project and preparing tender invitations for services required;

- ◆ obtaining information about architectural practices which had undertaken similar work;

- ◆ taking up references for any which had not worked for the authority before;

- ◆ drawing up a shortlist of firms to be invited to tender, including submission of method statement and fee bid;

- ◆ assessing the tenders and making the selection against a set of criteria which included price; and

- ◆ making the appointment.

The selection panel placed particular emphasis on the architectural practices' previous track record. The appointment was offered on the basis of a combined assessment of capability and price. In this case, the successful tenderer did not offer the lowest price.

4.15 Choosing consultants is particularly difficult because their remit may be hard to define clearly at the appointment stage. Clients and their project managers will need good contract management skills; they must be able to define clearly what each professional is required to do, and how they interact with other professions (Case Study 4.4). Failure to do so can lead to confusion of roles, duplication of effort, poorer outcomes and increased costs.

4.16 Authorities will need to consider a range of issues when they review their selection and appointment procedures (Box 4C). But the most critical issue is the extent to which quality and price have a bearing on the choice of consultants. For example, an authority commissioning a complex project will place greater emphasis on the quality of the consulant (Exhibit 4.2).

Case Study 4.4
Thurrock Borough Council housing
project

Clearly defined requirements avoid
confusion and ensure a successful
outcome.

The council needed help to assist the in-house technical team in drawing up the detailed information required to obtain tenders for a housing project. They adopted the following approach:

- ◆ the design team leader drew up a detailed list of drawings to be prepared with an estimate of the time required to prepare the information;

- ◆ one firm, with whom the authority had worked successfully in the past, was approached. An individual architect was nominated to undertake the task, working in his own office, but under the supervision of the in-house design team leader;

- ◆ a contract was negotiated and agreed on the basis of hourly rates for a fixed period, as generated by the drawing schedule; and

- ◆ an agreement was drawn up by the authority's solicitor.

The required package of work was completed successfully, on time and within the agreed budget. Because of continuing resource shortages, further work was carried out on a similar basis.

Box 4C
Selection and appointment of
consultants

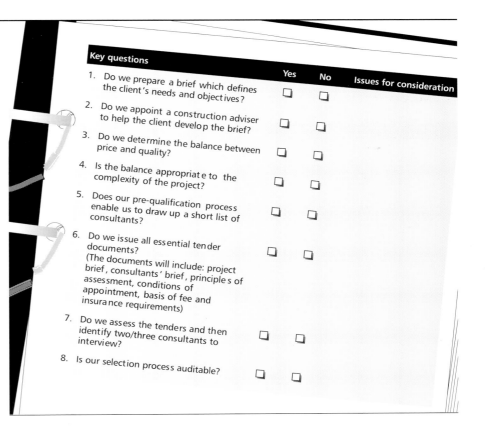

Exhibit 4.2
The relative importance of quality
and price

Authorities will need to consider a range
of issues.

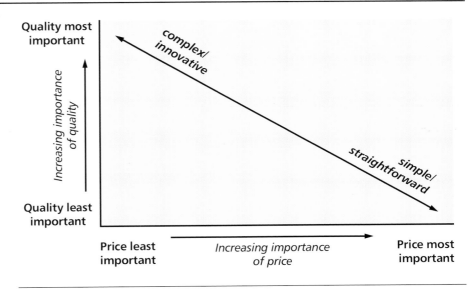

*Source: CIB – Selecting Consultants for the
Team: Balancing Quality and Price (Thomas
Telford Publishing – July 1996)*

Procurement of construction services

◆ How can we improve our procurement of all aspects of construction services?

4.17 Having decided on a traditional procurement system, authorities need to use an appropriate selection process to procure construction services. For most projects this will involve tendering. The construction phase of most local authority projects will not be covered by EU requirements (Ref. 11). Sometimes negotiation may be appropriate – for example, where a small amount of work follows on from a larger contract – but it should be the exception rather than the rule. The tender competition will ensure that the market is tested and that good value for money (VFM) is achieved through the selection process (Exhibit 4.3). 'Agree project brief' is discussed in detail in Chapter 3 (Option and Design Management). The other steps are outlined in the paragraphs that follow.

4.18 The role of elected members in tendering is important but limited. They should define and monitor the procedural framework (including tender limits) and the exception limits within which the process operates. Only in unusual circumstances, such as when there is a recommendation not to choose the lowest bid that meets the quality criteria, should they be further involved. But the fieldwork suggests that members often play a more active role. For example, at one metropolitan district, members have to approve the list of tenderers. This requirement can delay projects by several weeks.

Exhibit 4.3
Procuring construction services

Most projects will involve tendering.

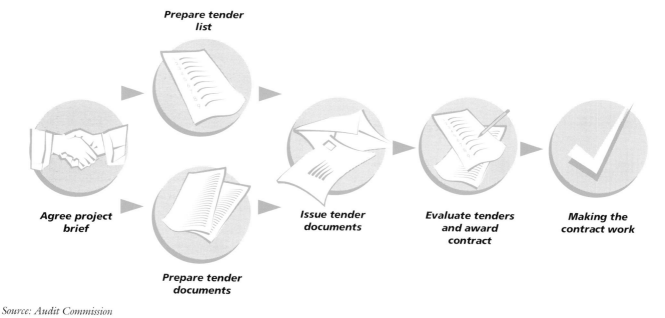

Prepare tender list

Agree project brief

Prepare tender documents

Issue tender documents

Evaluate tenders and award contract

Making the contract work

Source: Audit Commission

'Many authorities maintain an "approved list" to help them establish shortlists but fail to make best use of it...'

Prepare tender list

4.19 The number of tenderers invited to tender should be kept reasonably low to give contractors a reasonable chance of success and to reduce administrative costs. The NJCC Code of Procedure for Single Stage Selective Tendering recommends that a maximum of six firms be invited to tender, with two names in reserve in case any of the initial six decline to bid. Ideally, a shortlist should incorporate some contractors which have previously performed well, and some new contractors for comparison. A fieldwork authority established a good shortlist by allowing the design team to select three likely tenderers on the basis of their experience and then selecting three further tenderers randomly from an approved list of suitably qualified contractors.

4.20 Inadequate shortlisting procedures identified in the fieldwork included those which relied purely on professional judgement and were therefore open to question on both probity and VFM grounds, and others which, being purely random because of past accountability worries, failed to take advantage of professional judgement or good relationships built up over time with individual contractors.

4.21 Many authorities maintain an 'approved list' to help them establish shortlists but fail to make best use of it either because:

♦ the list is too large and is expensive to maintain. It is also costly to contractors who have to comply with pre-qualification requirements. The Construction Industry Board has developed a single pre-qualification document for the public sector (Appendix 1); or

♦ they tend to advertise too many contracts too widely. Thresholds for full external advertisement of tenders should not be set too low, since this will generate a lot of work, nor too high, since this runs the risk of not obtaining enough bids to achieve fully competitive results. Authorities vary in the threshold values they set for a full external advertisement of tenders. One county council set a limit of £20,000, a relatively low figure, which leads to burdensome procedures for officers. A unit of three staff is fully occupied in dealing with applicants and checking references.

Prepare tender documents

4.22 The tender documents convey to tenderers the intentions and requirements of the design. Fieldwork did not show significant problems in this area but in the construction industry inadequate information is the reason most frequently given for 'claims' submitted by contractors for the reimbursement of 'loss and expense'. Quality management procedures will generally ensure that tender documents are complete before contractors are invited to tender (Chapter 8).

Issue tender documents

4.23 Potential contractors need to be given adequate time to consider how to meet the project requirements and to calculate costs. Inadequate time for the tender period will mean that this process will be rushed, with either a premium on the price for uncalculated risk or an under-bid which leads to cost-cutting during the project to recoup a loss. The National Joint Consultative Committee for Building (NJCC) code for traditional contracts recommends a norm of 28 days for the tender period. But more than half of all projects surveyed had used shorter periods (Exhibit 4.4).

Evaluate tenders and award contracts

4.24 The lowest price need not necessarily be chosen automatically. But where thorough pre-qualification processes are in place, authorities will need to justify not accepting the lowest tender. However, very low tenders should be evaluated rigorously to make sure that they meet the required quality standards. The successful contractor must be notified and given time to mobilise resources to start on site. But unsuccessful tenderers must also be notified and debriefed. This is generally helpful to tenderers and can only help in developing good working relationships with contractors.

Making the contract work

4.25 The Latham Report is clear that better relationships must replace the traditional antagonism between clients and contractors if better value for money is to be achieved in construction. If authorities adopt an approach akin to that advocated by Latham, they will have to work more closely with professionals and contractors, and develop different ways of managing their relationships (Ref. 2). The problem of adversarial relationships concerns not just the form of contract. The problem is one of culture and trading relationships. Changing the form of contract will solve nothing if authorities are interested only in avoiding risk, and contractors are determined to press claims. A commitment to developing a partnership and making it work is also required.

4.26 Local contractors often have a long-term interest in developing good working relationships with authorities. But in seeking the benefits of closer working, authorities must also maintain high standards of public accountability, including benefiting from competition. In the public sector, a partnering style of working is more appropriate after appointing a contractor through competition (Box 4D, overleaf). While the potential benefits are considerable, robust procedures are needed to ensure probity. Earlier regular involvement by internal audit could be an appropriate response.

Exhibit 4.4
Tendering periods

For over half of the contracts the time allowed for contractors to tender is below the recommended industry norm of 28 days.

Tendering for contracts over £500,000

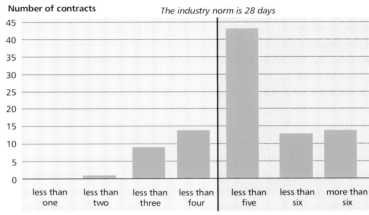

Tendering periods for contracts between £100,000 and £500,000

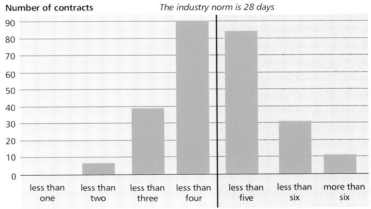

Tendering periods for contracts between £25,000 and £100,000

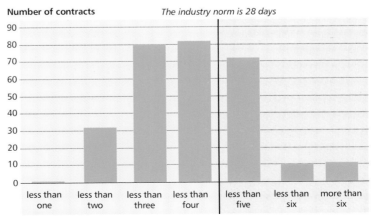

Source: Audit Commission survey

Box 4D
Making the contract work

Partnering: essential procedures	
Selection of contractors	Procedures are constructed to ensure that the parties are compatible and committed to partnering. This is likely to involve a two-staged approach to the selection of contractors. At the first stage, contractors are selected by questionnaire and interview. The second stage selection is by tender.
Workshop	All parties and stakeholders attend workshops at which objectives for project(s) and ground rules are agreed.
Charter	A charter incorporating the objectives and ground rules is drawn up. It does not supersede the contract but it sets out the working relationships. It is a statement of how the parties will conduct themselves.
Communications	Clear and open communications are a critical element of partnering. The communications systems will be agreed at the workshop.
Monitoring	Continuous monitoring of performance is essential to ensure that partnering is successful in achieving its objectives and those of the project(s). But monitoring must include a commitment to improve performance.
Avoidance and resolution of disputes	Jointly agreed procedures to avoid disputes and resolve issues are needed/advisable to ensure that any disputes are resolved at the lowest possible level.

4.27 Post-contract partnering is compatible with compulsory competitive tendering (CCT). However, authorities will need to make sure that tenderers are made aware of the intent to enter into post-contract partnering prior to or with the invitation to tender and that arrangements do not favour one bidder over others, if they are to comply with the Department of the Environment's statutory guidance on CCT (Ref. 12). Partnering is also acceptable under EU rules if:

◆ it is competitively arranged;

◆ the client's needs and objectives are clearly stated;

◆ the contract is for a specified period; and

◆ safeguards for future competition are incorporated.

The Department of the Environment has commissioned the European Construction Institute to publish a partnering tool-kit for the public sector. The tool-kit provides authorities with advice on the appropriate approach (Ref. 13).

Selection and appointment of subcontractors

4.28 A significant proportion of work on site is now carried out by subcontractors. Specialist suppliers and subcontractors are also making an increasingly important contribution to design, particularly on major projects. Integrating the contribution of subcontractors, and in particular the design undertaken by specialists, is a critical component of successful procurement. It is therefore essential that this is recognised in the contract documents. If the main contract precludes responsibility for design on the part of the main

'Where nomination procedures are used, they should be implemented in full, with subcontracts tendered and agreed prior to accepting the tender for the main contract.'

contractor, responsibility for the design of specialist elements must be covered by the use of nomination procedures or by the contractor's Design Portion Supplement (separately for each specialist item) – Appendix 4. Where nomination procedures are used, they should be implemented in full, with subcontracts tendered and agreed prior to accepting the tender for the main contract.

Contracts legislation

4.29 The Housing Grants, Construction and Regeneration Act 1996 received Royal Assent in July 1996. Part II of the Act provides, as suggested by the Latham review, a framework for fairer contracts and better working relationships within the construction industry. The Act specifies that contracts will contain certain provisions relating to adjudication and payment, and that – where they do not – parties may rely on fall-back provisions contained in regulations made by the Secretary of State for the Environment. When the regulations come into force they will affect the standard forms of contracts used by authorities. The Department of the Environment has consulted on its proposals for the regulations which are likely to be implemented in 1997. A summary of the implications for authorities is contained in Appendix 2.

Checklist for action

Aspects of performance	Good practice features	Current practice	Action
Procurement approach	Approach the selection of procurement system systematically.		
	Use nomination procedures for the appointment of subcontractors or specialists prior to accepting the tender for the main contract. But allow the main contractor to tender on the basis of using a firm of its choice.		
Phasing/ packaging work	Package/phase work to meet needs of clients/users.		
	Optimise size of contract to get best value.		
Technical/ professional services	Identify/plan technical and professional services at project inception.		
Appointing consultants	Appoint consultants on the basis of quality and price.		
	Define clearly the consultants' remit.		
Tendering procedures	Members define procedural framework and monitor its application.		
	Operate a small approved list.		
	Set appropriate thresholds for open advertising.		
	Provide all necessary documentation on time.		
	Allow at least four weeks for tendering.		
Partnering	Implement a post-contract partnering approach.		
	Maintain probity and accountability.		

5 Time Management

The key processes that enable the consistent delivery of projects to time are:

- establishing project programmes and systems that incorporate all relevant inputs, activities, milestones and constraints;

- monitoring progress against the programme; and

- reporting to all who need to be kept informed so that appropriate action may be taken in the event of unavoidable delays.

Planning takes time, but it is essential for ultimate success and for achieving value for money. The golden rule of the six Ps – prior preparation and planning prevents poor performance – applies particularly to capital projects. However, planning time is frequently constrained by funding deadlines. Design teams are under considerable pressure to produce designs and other information and tendering periods are often cut below recommended levels. The impact of inadequate time management of individual projects extends beyond the projects themselves. Slippage or other changes can affect cashflows and the application of resources, and impact on authorities' overall capital programmes. Authorities should balance the benefits of progressing projects so that they are ready to go ahead as soon as resources are available against the risk of spending money on abortive work.

Managing time during construction is also critical to a successful outcome. But the survey of 700 projects suggests that improvements can be made – two-thirds of projects ran late and authorities appeared to accept responsibility for the delays for 75 per cent of them.

This chapter considers these issues and makes the following recommendations.

Authorities should:	*This will have the following benefits:*
◆ balance the risks of making time for design early on, against the potential cost of abortive work on projects that do not subsequently get funding approval	◆ minimise losses and improve value for money
◆ allow sufficient time for detailed design and consultation with clients and users	◆ greater opportunity to reduce costs and avoid mistakes at the start of a project
◆ review systems for monitoring and reporting of progress during design, tendering and construction	◆ problems can be identified and resolved promptly, and any spare resources reallocated to other projects

Project programme

◆ Does each project have an agreed programme which identifies activities and constraints and target dates?

5.1 Planning takes time, but it is essential for ultimate success and for achieving value for money. Although some fieldwork authorities begin to plan projects once they have been included in their capital programmes, others do not allow detailed design to start until funding for the project is secure. This is understandable, as authorities may be reluctant to incur design costs on projects that are not certain to go ahead. But apparent caution can lead to ineffective project programmes. In particular, insufficient time allowed during the inception and design stages will increase the risk of both time and cost overruns during construction, and poor user satisfaction. Affordability is, of course, important. Expenditure on planning and design must be balanced against a judgement of available resources.

5.2 The hallmark of a well-managed project is the delivery of its planned objectives to the right quality, on time and within budget (Chapter 6). Authorities generally work hard to deliver projects to the right quality, particularly by involving users (Chapters 2 and 3). However, two-thirds of projects surveyed by the Audit Commission were completed late and half of all

Exhibit 5.1
Construction period as a percentage of planned period

Two-thirds of projects ran late.

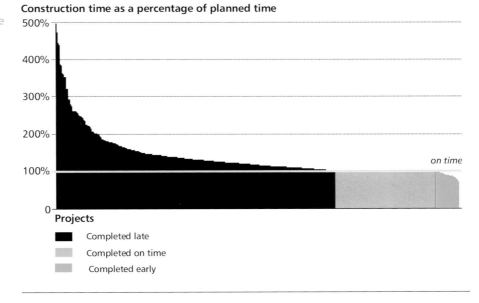

Construction time as a percentage of planned time

on time

Projects

◼ Completed late

▨ Completed on time

▩ Completed early

Source: Audit Commission survey

the projects were 15 per cent or more behind schedule (Exhibit 5.1). Authorities extended the contract period to cover the whole delay in 75 per cent of projects which overran and imposed liquidated and ascertained damages in fewer than half the others. This practice suggests that authorities accepted that the delays were generally out of the contractors' control.

5.3 Good time management arrangements will help to reduce the risk of projects running late by:

◆ establishing a project programme that incorporates all relevant inputs, activities and constraints;

◆ monitoring progress against the programme; and

◆ reporting to all those involved in the project.

5.4 The detail and rigour of the procedures necessary for an authority to manage project timescales effectively will depend on the scale and circumstances of each project. But key principles need to be followed in all cases. A member of the project team, generally the project manager, is given responsibility for:

◆ compiling the overall project programme, which is discussed and agreed with the project stakeholders;

◆ identifying the critical activities that will deliver the project and their inter-relationship;

◆ monitoring and reporting progress against the programme; and

◆ managing the consequences of changes to the programme and updating it as necessary.

5.5 During key stages of the project development process, particular responsibility for time management is devolved to the design team leader

'The relevant project activities and constraints must be combined into a project programme that meets the required target dates, and is made available to the project team...'

(during the design and tender stage) and to the contractor (during the construction stage). However, the project manager maintains overall control by setting the parameters within which the design team leader and the contractor will compile their detailed programmes.

5.6 The relevant project activities and constraints must be combined into a project programme that meets the required target dates, and is made available to the project team (Chapter 2) in a suitable format. The nature of the process and the output will vary widely. For many small or straightforward projects, a simple list of key target dates will do. As a minimum the following should be identified:

- appointing the design team;
- completing the client's brief;
- completing and approving the design/specification;
- completing tender documents, inviting tenders;
- appointing the contractor; and
- completing the works.

5.7 For larger or more complex projects, a chart which shows milestones, duration and relationship of activities will help management processes (Exhibit 5.2). More sophisticated computer-based techniques are available which use project management software and these are particularly appropriate for the

Exhibit 5.2
Project plan for the construction of local offices

For larger or more complex projects, a chart that shows milestones, duration and relationship of activities will help management processes.

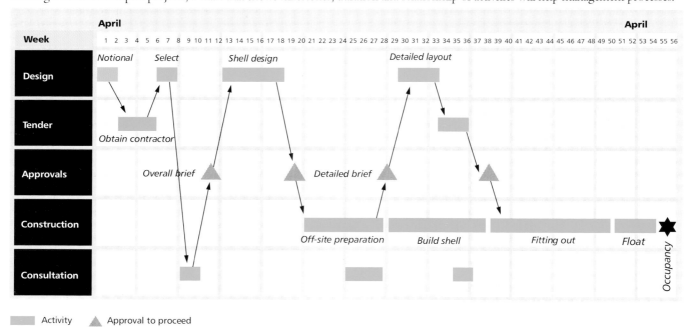

Activity   Approval to proceed

Source: Audit Commission adaptation of a project undertaken by a London borough

larger projects carried out by local authorities. In all cases, a key requirement is to allow enough time for all critical activities. But fieldwork authorities frequently allowed funding deadlines to constrain project programmes. In some cases, the whole project was driven by only a small proportion of the budget (Case Study 5.1). In other cases, funding deadlines were not sufficiently well recognised in the project programmes.

5.8 Allowing sufficient time for tendering the construction contract is a critical element in compiling the project programme, and in many cases the time allowed by many authorities is too short in comparison with nationally agreed criteria (Chapter 4). But once tenders have been accepted, a reasonable period of time, which is neither too long nor too short, should be included in the programme to enable the contractor to mobilise resources before starting on site. Although there are no nationally agreed benchmarks, mobilisation periods in the range of one to three months provide contractors with a reasonable period in which to organise their resources. The survey authorities had mobilisation periods which ranged from a few days to over 12 months (Exhibit 5.3, overleaf).

Case Study 5.1
Construction of a sports centre

An unrealistic assessment of risk can distort the design and tender programme.

As part of a well-considered leisure strategy, an authority planned the construction of a sports centre with an initial capital budget of £1.66 million. The proposal and design were developed with input from the Sports Council, which offered a grant of £100,000.

The design and tender programme was driven to an unrealistic extent by the council's concern over the risk, perceived at the time, of a moratorium on local authority capital expenditure. As a result:

◆ site investigation was not complete at tender (notwithstanding known high risks);

◆ half of the bill items were not measured; and

◆ no pre-tender estimate was carried out.

The lowest tender was £2.16 million. The council decided at first to postpone the construction contract, but shortly afterwards resolved to proceed when it became clear that the Sports Council grant would otherwise be lost. As a result, the contract was placed for £2 million in the context of considerable risk. In the event, the contractor was pro-active in resolving problems, and the out-turn was satisfactory. With another contractor the final account might have been very different, with the Sports Council contribution more than absorbed by 'claims'.

Exhibit 5.3
Mobilisation periods

There is wide variation in mobilisation periods.

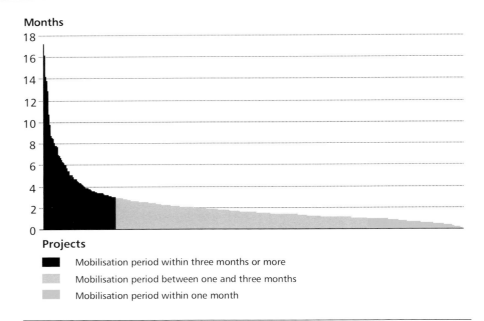

Months

Projects

Mobilisation period within three months or more

Mobilisation period between one and three months

Mobilisation period within one month

Source: Audit Commission survey

Monitoring

◆ How do we make sure that projects stay on schedule?

5.9 Once the overall project programme has been agreed, progress needs to be monitored. But authorities too often start monitoring progress only after work has started on site. This is too late, as activities undertaken during the design and tendering stages can have an impact on the timely completion of projects. Monitoring progress should therefore start at the earliest opportunity – at project inception. The task should be allocated to the project manager who acts as the client's agent.

5.10 The project manager should monitor overall progress regularly against the project programme. But the frequency should normally be monthly to coincide with monthly valuations. More frequent monitoring might be appropriate for complex projects, or for those with particular time constraints.

5.11 The design team leader and the contractor also have a role to play in monitoring performance against the programme. The design team leader needs to keep progress during the design and tendering stages constantly under review and should hold regular design team meetings. But the design team is also responsible for monitoring performance during the construction stage. For all but small or very straightforward projects, the design team should meet regularly with the contractor to:

◆ discuss progress on individual items;

◆ review the overall position and anticipated completion;

◆ identify reasons for delay(s); and

◆ identify necessary actions including response to delay.

There are various tools to help:

Information systems

5.12 Good management is impossible unless authorities have good management information systems to control the progress of projects. The Commission's survey requested information that authorities would need as a matter of course to monitor and review projects (Box 5A). Although all the authorities in the survey volunteered to take part, more than one-fifth were unable to provide the data requested. Some of the returns that were provided were incomplete in material details. For example, some authorities were unable to give key dates, such as when the scheme design approval was given, or the planned date for starting work on site.

5.13 A project manager in one authority said: 'On the basis of my experience, including the private sector, I thought this authority was good at managing its projects. The Commission's survey poses straightforward data requests to which it should be easy to respond. But we have found it so difficult that I am now doubtful as to how well we are managing.'

Cashflow

5.14 All authorities collect and report information during the life of a project as part of the process of valuing work done by, and payments due to, contractors. But many authorities do not use such information as a spur to action. For example, authorities can use forecasts of project cashflow to give early warning of delays – actual payments falling below predicted levels is normally a reliable indicator that progress is falling behind schedule (Table 5.1, overleaf).

Contractor's reports

5.15 The detailed programme for construction works, which is drawn up by the contractor, is primarily the contractor's tool for managing their own area of responsibility. It also provides the basis for monitoring and reporting on progress on site. Construction contracts should therefore specify the contractor's provision of a programme at the start of the contract and in an agreed format.

Box 5A
Key dates for monitoring performance

An unrealistic assessment of risk can distort the design and tender programme.

- Date of scheme design approval
- Date planned at scheme design approval stage for start on site
- Date planned at scheme design approval state for completion
- Date of invitation to tender
- Date for receipt of tenders
- Date of contract start
- Date of contract completion
- Date of extended completion
- Date of practical completion
- Date of final account

Table 5.1
Average construction expenditure
per month

Authorities do not use all available
information to identify potential
problems.

		Planned expenditure per month £'000	Actual expenditure per month £'000	Percentage spent each month
All projects		46.5	36.9	79%
By value	£25,000 – £100,000	27.3	19.5	71%
	£100,000 – £500,000	51.1	41.0	80%
	Over £500,000	105.0	91.6	86%
By type	New-build	56.3	47.6	85%
	Refurbishment	42.6	34.0	80%
	Mechanical and electrical	42.2	28.9	68%
	External works	52.9	40.2	76%

Note:
Planned expenditure per month = contract sum divided by contract period
Actual expenditure = outturn cost divided by actual construction period
Percentage spent = actual expenditure as percentage of planned expenditure

Source: Audit Commission survey

5.16 The contract should also specify how the contractor is required to report on progress. This will normally be a schedule of the activities expressed in the programme, reporting for each the percentages scheduled and actually achieved. The report should include:

♦ an assessment of overall progress with reference to critical activities;

♦ relevant explanations of the causes of any delay;

♦ a forecast completion date; and

♦ how often reports should be submitted.

The reports are normally considered at progress meetings with the design team (for all but small or straightforward projects the design team should meet the contractor monthly).

Reporting

♦ Do we receive appropriate, clear and timely reports on progress?

5.17 Arrangements for reporting progress will depend on the extent of delegation within the authority and the level of management to which reports are made (Exhibit 5.4). Reporting on progress should take place at the same time as reports on project costs (Chapter 6). The reporting requirements for each level of management are:

Project manager

♦ design team leader reports in detail on progress against the design and tender programme and, in particular, on changes made to the programme;

♦ contractor reports against construction programme milestones; reports to include commentary on delays and forecast completion date;

♦ project team meetings to review progress, discuss and resolve issues; and

♦ monitoring takes place monthly but more frequently for sensitive, large or complex projects.

Exhibit 5.4
Reporting to the different levels of management

Reporting on progress and costs should take place at the same time.

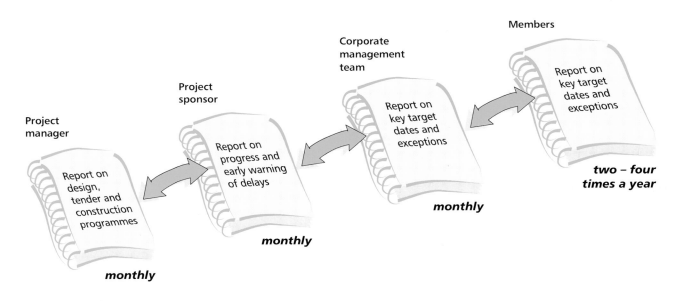

Source: Audit Commission

Project sponsor

- ◆ project manager reports on progress against the overall project programme for each project;
- ◆ project manager provides early indication of possible delays to projects; and
- ◆ monitoring takes place monthly but more frequently for sensitive, large or complex projects.

Corporate management team

- ◆ project sponsors report on progress against critical key target dates for each project, but in the context of the authority's overall capital programme; and
- ◆ monitoring takes place monthly. Exception reports prepared in repect of sensitive, large or complex projects.

Members

- ◆ officers report on progress against critical key target dates for each project, but in the context of the authority's overall capital programme. Reports produced between two to four times a year; and
- ◆ exception reports produced as and when required to resolve issues that could give rise to delays.

Checklist for action

Aspects of performance	Good practice features	Current practice	Action
Making time to plan and deliver projects	Balance risk of not making time for design against the cost of abortive design work.		
	Establish an overall project programme which identifies activities and constraints and is agreed by the project team. Appropriate level of detail shown for the size and complexity of the project.		
	Design team leader should prepare detailed programme for design and tender.		
	Contractor should prepare detailed construction programme as specified in the contract.		
	Give successful tenderers time to mobilise resources.		
Delivering projects on time	Allocate responsibilities for monitoring.		
	Implement systems for monitoring performance against project programmes.		
	Provide information systems that enable effective monitoring.		
	Use information that is already available to highlight problems.		
	Report on progress regularly but match level of detail and frequency to the level of management.		

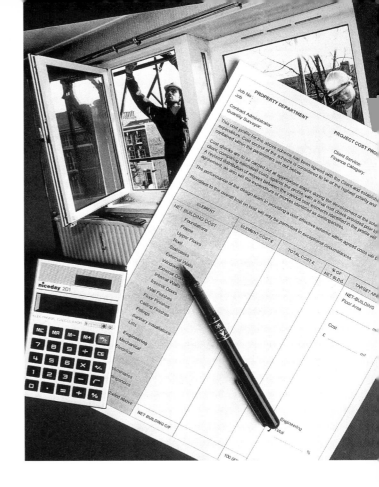

6 Cost Management

Effective management of project costs is essential to achieve value for money, in particular to:

- complete projects within allocated budgets;

- provide clients with a realistic degree of control over expenditure, and avoid unnecessary, abortive or unauthorised expenditure;

- secure a balance between resources and expenditure at programme level; and

- enable the authority as client to take informed decisions on priorities.

The disciplined management of the cost of individual projects is not only essential to their successful outcome but also to the management of the capital programme. However, for some authorities, 'spending up' to their annual capital allocation is taking priority over getting project budgets right or controlling actual costs. This view is supported by the results of the survey of 700 projects:

- *in more than half, estimates were not adjusted as projects progressed and in two out of five there was a difference of more than 15 per cent between the project estimate and the tender price. Significant differences between project budgets and tender prices carry a number of risks. If budgets are too low, projects require redesign and other steps to reduce costs. On the other hand, budgets that are too high tie up resources that should have been available for other projects and reduces the need to seek value for money;*

- *the costs of technical services were not controlled as well as they could. Fees ranged from 2 per cent to over 35 per cent of construction costs. Some authorities excluded the cost of technical services from project costs; and*

- *in half the projects, the difference between actual construction costs and the contract sum was greater than 5 per cent.*

This chapter considers these issues and makes the following recommendations.

Authorities should:	This will have the following benefits:
• review procedures for setting and updating project budgets	• improve project authorisation and monitoring; ensure more effective and efficient allocation of capital resources
• manage costs during design by applying cost-planning techniques in a rigorous manner, using the most up-to-date information available	• designs developed in line with agreed budgets; late changes avoided; and changes in scope made by clients taken into account
• include the estimated cost of technical services in project budgets and monitor actual costs during design and construction	• more cost-effective use of technical services
• implement procedures for monitoring and reporting on costs during construction	• minimises the risk of increased costs during construction; better basis for considering the impact of change.
• include contingency sums within a contract only as part of a disciplined process of risk management	• prevents contingency sums being used as a substitute for good design or clarifies the value or extent of work prior to tender

Setting realistic project budgets

♦ How realistic are our project budgets?

♦ To what extent do budget approvals give staff the authority to proceed with a project?

♦ Do we use cost-planning techniques?

♦ Are contingencies used as a subsititute for good planning?

6.1 Managing the cost of individual projects is essential not only for the successful outcome of those projects, but also for the satisfactory management of the capital programme as a whole (Chapter 1). Authorities are concerned to spend their annual allocation of borrowing approval. Given the constraints on capital resources, this is understandable. However, for some, 'spending up' is taking priority over getting project budgets right or controlling costs. This partly explains why one-quarter of the projects that were surveyed by the Audit Commission cost more than 5 per cent above their initial contract sum and one-quarter more than 5 per cent below (Exhibit 6.1). Projects which are underspent do not necessarily represent a successful outcome, since the unused resources earmarked for these projects could have been put to better use earlier. In addition, the contract sum may have included a significant level of contingencies that were not needed.

6.2 So managing project costs is important; this means more than just controlling construction costs. Project costs must be managed from the outset – that is, from inception when the project budget is first set, through the design stage when the budget is firmed up, to completion. But the Audit Commission's survey of 700 projects suggests that at some authorities the budgeting process is not as robust as it could be. In two out of five projects the difference between the tender sum and the scheme design estimate was more than 15 per cent of the scheme design estimate (Exhibit 6.2, overleaf). Fluctuations in the state of the construction industry may account for some of the difference. However, setting estimates too high ties up resources which could be used for other projects and it also reduces the incentives for achieving best value for money. On the other hand, when estimates are set too low, late changes are ususally made to the scope of a project as a way of reducing costs or other planned projects are delayed.

Exhibit 6.1
Outturn contract sum compared with agreed contract sum

One-quarter of projects cost more than 5 per cent above the contract sum and one-quarter more than 5 per cent below.

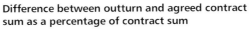
Difference between outturn and agreed contract sum as a percentage of contract sum

Projects
Cost increased by more than 5%
Cost within 5%
Cost decreased by more than 5%

Source: Audit Commission survey

Exhibit 6.2
Tender sum compared with the
scheme design estimate

The difference between the tender sum and
the scheme design estimate was more than
15 per cent of the scheme design estimate
for 40 per cent of projects.

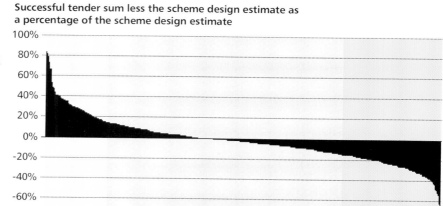

**Successful tender sum less the scheme design estimate as
a percentage of the scheme design estimate**

Projects

16% of tender sums higher than the scheme design estimate by more than 15%

59% of scheme design estimates within + or - 15%

25% of tender sums lower than the scheme design estimate by more than 15%

Source: Audit Commission survey

6.3 The fieldwork authorities had widely different levels of performance in setting project budgets. Some authorities had specific procedures in place to ensure that estimates were sound before a project could be committed to the capital programme (Case Study 6.1). Significantly, where funding deadlines imposed tight timescales, estimates were shown to be too low upon receipt of tenders, requiring redesign and other steps to reduce costs.

6.4 The best performers at keeping costs to budget were those authorities which set their project budgets systematically. For example, budgets:

♦ were based on a firm and clear statement of the client requirements. These requirements covered, as a minimum, the scheme objectives; the scope, such as the total floor area; and the general level of quality;

Case Study 6.1
Project budgets

Project budgets are set by staff with
appropriate skills and training.

Essex County Council requires that all projects are properly appraised before the overall capital programme is approved. Appraisals are made firstly at departmental level and then reviewed by the cross-departmental Capital Programme Management Team, chaired by the Deputy County Treasurer.

As part of the process, all project budgets are prepared by the Building Economics Unit under the direction of the chief quantity surveyor, in accordance with performance and quality standards that are reviewed annually for value for money.

◆ were calculated on an appropriate basis. Initial estimates might be based on global measures, such as the cost per square metre. Subsequent estimates can be more refined and based on approximate or measured unit rates developed by the authority or available nationally, such as the detailed unit costs produced by the Department for Education and Employment for school buildings;

◆ included all costs attributable to the project. The cost of construction work is the largest component, but there is always a cost for technical services and there may be a cost for relocating existing tenants, etc; and

◆ had contingencies that were realistic and based on assessment of risk, rather than being a substitute for poor and/or incomplete designs.

6.5 The preparation of accurate budget estimates requires skills. Individuals responsible should be qualified for the task, by training or relevant experience. They must have access to reliable and relevant data. But it is also good practice for the authority to benchmark its cost data for typical buildings or elements against the best of what is being achieved elsewhere. For example, the Department for Education and Employment publishes a quarterly report on education building projects (Ref. 14).

Timing of budget approval

6.6 A project is costed (*the initial estimate*) and approved at the point of entry into the capital programme. But as explained above, the budget will need to be updated at potentially two key stages:

◆ *scheme design estimate* – based on firm views of design proposals, but prior to significant design effort; and

◆ *pre-tender estimate* – based on detailed drawings, specifications, etc, prepared for tender purposes (that is, immediately prior to commitment to construction).

6.7 But in half of all projects surveyed by the Audit Commission there is no evidence that project budgets were updated between the initial estimate at inception, the scheme design estimate and the pre-tender estimate (Exhibit 6.3, overleaf).

6.8 Procedures should also be in place to manage costs in the event of changes to the client's brief, funding, or any other factor affecting design. The cost implications should be estimated prior to implementation by the design team and any changes agreed with the client.

Cost planning

6.9 Cost planning is a well-established technique in which the overall budget is broken down into the component parts of the project. The cost plan is an essential and integral part of the development of the project, helping to integrate design and cost considerations, and to clarify the client's priorities as early as possible. Effective cost planning helps to prevent big differences between final estimates and tenders.

'The cost plan is an essential and integral part of the development of the project, helping to integrate design and cost considerations, and to clarify the client's priorities as early as possible.'

Exhibit 6.3
Updating cost estimates

Cost estimates for half of all projects are not updated between the initial estimate and the scheme design.

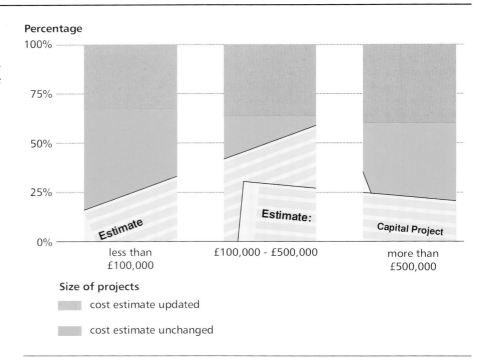

Percentage

Size of projects

cost estimate updated

cost estimate unchanged

Source: Audit Commission survey

6.10 The value of cost planning is widely recognised by technical staff in local authorities, but the technique was rarely used at the fieldwork authorities. Formal cost planning is clearly not necessary in many small or straightforward projects, but the study team found a number of situations where cost planning was not undertaken, and where it might have avoided subsequent difficulties in staying within the budget (typically in the context of tight timescales). At West Sussex County Council, for example, the design team obtain the client's approval to the 'cost profile', with further approval required if any material changes are made during design or construction (Exhibit 6.4).

6.11 If the nature of the project is such that its design undergoes a process of development, the leader of the design team, with the cost consultant, should carry out regular checks on the cost implications. Final cost planning is likely to be appropriate on such projects, and cost checking will be integral to this process. Otherwise, as a minimum, cost checks should take place at key stages:

◆ completion of scheme design;

◆ completion of detailed design; and

◆ prior to tender.

Contingencies

6.12 Many contracts include contingency sums. Their inclusion should be part of a disciplined process of risk management (Chapter 7) and should not be seen as a substitute for good planning and budget setting. But any contingency should be pitched at an appropriate level and be subject to clear policies about how it may be spent.

Exhibit 6.4
Cost plan used by West Sussex County Council

The cost plan is an essential and integral part of the development of a project.

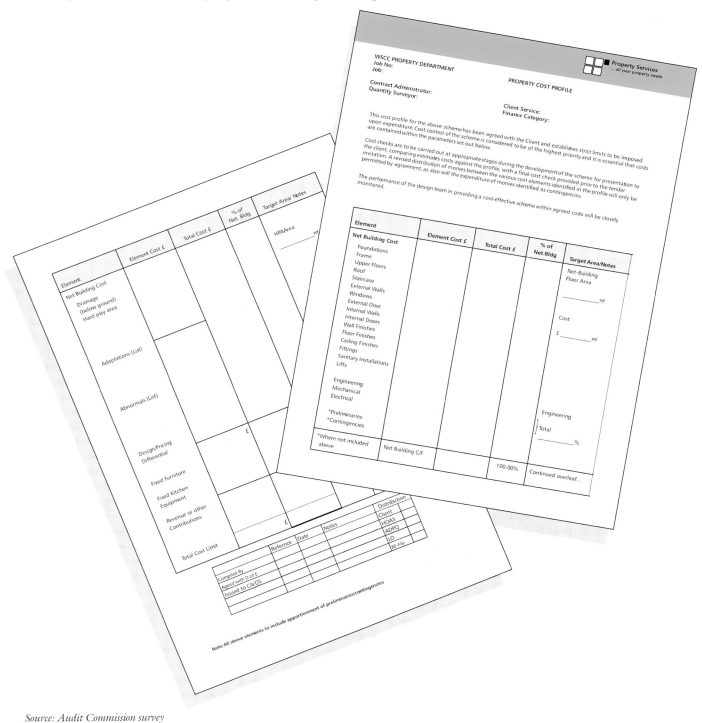

Source: Audit Commission survey

Cost of technical services

◆ Do we allocate the full cost of technical services to our projects?

6.13 In practice, the cost of technical services can be a substantial part of the overall cost of a project. The Audit Commission's survey has shown that there is wide variation in the level of fees charged to projects (Table 6.1). There is no correlation between fee levels and the use of internal or external consultants. Nor is there any link between fee levels and time or cost overruns. This latter fact suggests that many who pay high fee levels fail to get commensurate value from them. Fee levels range from under 2 per cent of the contract cost to 43 per cent (Exhibit 6.5). But a significant minority of authorities (15 per cent) do not identify or allocate the costs of technical services to their projects.

6.14 More detailed analysis of the Commission's survey shows that projects with fee levels above median values were not uniformly spread throughout the authorities surveyed. All the projects in one authority, for example, were above the median, whereas the project fee levels in seven others fell below the median. This would seem to indicate that effective management of the fee process is more important than who provides the consultancy service.

6.15 Pricing fees as a percentage of project cost, for example, gives consultants little incentive to control the overall cost of the scheme and is discouraged by the Construction Industry Board. It is generally recognised that prime cost or lump-sum pricing of consultancy services gives the client greater control (Refs. 9 and 10).

6.16 Another way that authorities can obtain better value for money in this area is by taking advantage of competition in fee levels to reduce costs (Chapter 4). But very low fees are not always an indicator of efficiency. They may, for example, be concealing a proper allocation of costs. Low fees can also be a false economy if professionals are always encouraged to take the quickest solution rather than looking for the most cost-effective one for the project as a whole.

6.17 Compulsory competitive tendering (CCT) is making local authorities review the cost of their technical services. Fees will be a particular focus of attention during the local audits of capital expenditure.

Table 6.1
Fees as a percentage of contract sum

There is wide variation in the level of fees charged to projects.

Source: Audit Commission survey

	New-build	Renovation	Mechanical and electrical	External works
Minimum	2	2	1	4
Lower quartile	11	9	7	8
Median	15	13	9	11
Upper quartile	19	17	13	15
Maximum	29	43	33	43

Exhibit 6.5
Fee percentage and contract sum

There is a wide variation in the level of fees charged to projects.

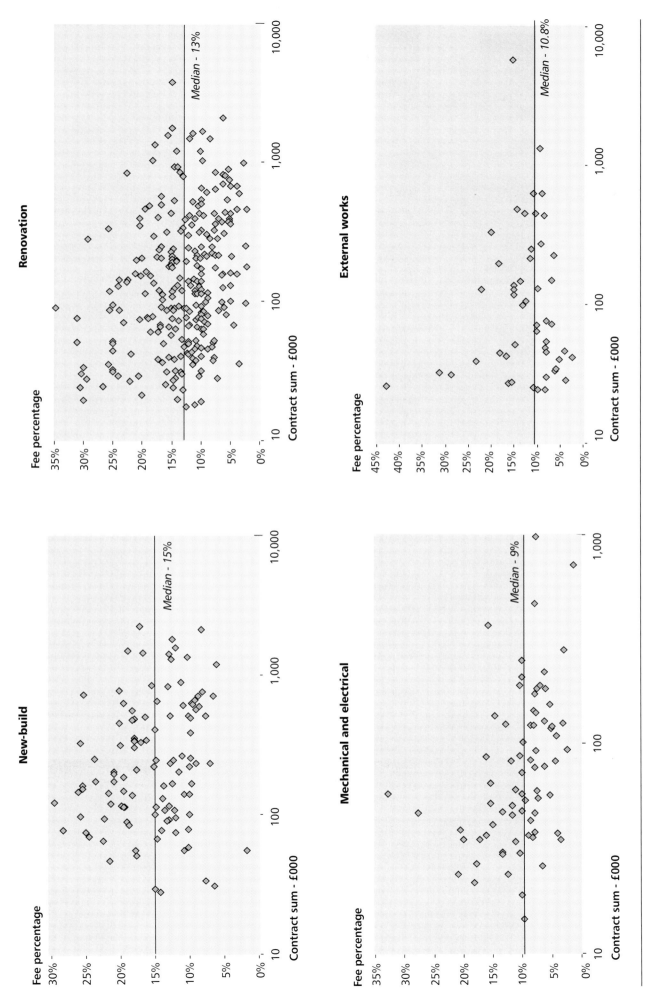

93

Monitoring the cost of construction

◆ How do we make sure that project costs do not exceed the contract sum?

6.18 In the majority of contracts placed by authorities:

◆ a variation in the final sum payable to the contractor is possible under the terms of the contract; and

◆ payments are made on a staged basis.

It is therefore essential that the cost of construction is monitored regularly in respect of the staged payments made to date and the forecast outturn cost. Monitoring should be carried out monthly (matching the normal cycle of valuation work undertaken for the purpose of contractual payment to the contractor) by an individual who is technically qualified to do so. Monitoring of costs and time (Chapter 5) should be done together. Key cost variables should form part of the monitoring process (Box 6A)

6.19 For monitoring to be reliable, the cost consultant must follow basic good practice in keeping up to date with the remeasurement of provisional quantities, provisional sums and variations. This will also facilitate the rapid settlement of final accounts (Chapter 2).

Cost of change during construction

6.20 In most contracts, variation in the final sum payable to the contractor is possible under the terms of the contract. Variations may arise from:

◆ *shortcomings in the design information* – such as structural work which is inaccurately specified – should be actioned immediately by the design team and reported retrospectively if it is necessary to avoid delay, but otherwise the client's agreement should be sought first;

◆ *unavoidable changes* – such as redesign in response to unforeseen ground conditions or defects in existing buildings – should be actioned immediately by the design team and reported retrospectively if it is necessary to avoid delay, but otherwise the client's agreement should be sought first;

◆ *relatively minor items* – that can be actioned immediately by the design team within available contingency sums; and

◆ *optional items* – in technical terms, these include changes requested by the client. The cost of these should be estimated by the cost consultant for client approval prior to implementation, and the project budget adjusted accordingly. Pre-pricing by the contractor gives greater cost certainty but at the risk of delay and/or high pricing as a result of pressure on time.

Box 6A
Key cost variables

◆ money spent and committed to date

◆ expenditure of provisional sum

◆ adjustments relating to prime cost sums

◆ status of contingency sum

◆ net cost of variations to date

◆ net cost of anticipated variations

◆ notified and anticipated claims by the contractor

◆ anticipated final cost

6.21 The cost of a variation should be obtained from the contractor before giving the go ahead for it to be undertaken. If there is an apparent need to increase the budget, the design team should identify options for making compensating savings.

6.22 To keep variations to a minimum, there should be formal approval procedures, with a requirement that significant changes be signed off by the project sponsor or the project manager. Minor variations should also be reported to the sponsor. Records of progress on the contract, including all variations, should be maintained in a systematic way. This is particularly important so that authorities can respond appropriately to any future claims by contractors and to facilitate post-project review and audit.

6.23 In general, authorities had clear procedures in standing orders and financial regulations to control variations. But success in applying the procedures in practice was variable, even for different projects within the same authority. Sometimes the formal approval procedures were invoked to give retrospective sanction to actions which had already taken place.

Reporting

◆ Are arrangements in place for all levels of management to receive clear, complete and timely cost reports?

6.24 Arrangements for reporting budgets and outturn will depend on the extent of delegation within the authority and the level of management to which reports are made (Exhibit 6.6, overleaf). Reporting on progress should take place at the same time as reports on project time (Chapter 5). The reporting requirements for each level of management are:

Project manager
◆ design team leader reports in detail on costs against the contract sum;
◆ project manager receives reports on fees from the design team leader;
◆ project team meets to review costs, and to discuss and resolve any issues;
◆ monitoring takes place monthly but more frequently for sensitive, large or complex projects;
◆ design team leader reports on budget at inception, scheme design and at pre-tender stages; and
◆ design team leader signs off final account.

Project sponsor
◆ project manager reports on total project costs (including fees) in summarised form for each project;
◆ project manager provides early indication of possible increases/decreases to costs;
◆ monitoring takes place monthly but more frequently for sensitive, large or complex projects;
◆ project manager reports on budget at inception, scheme design and at pre-tender stages; and
◆ project manager reports on final account costs for each project.

Exhibit 6.6
Reporting to the different levels of management

Reporting on progress and costs should take place at the same time.

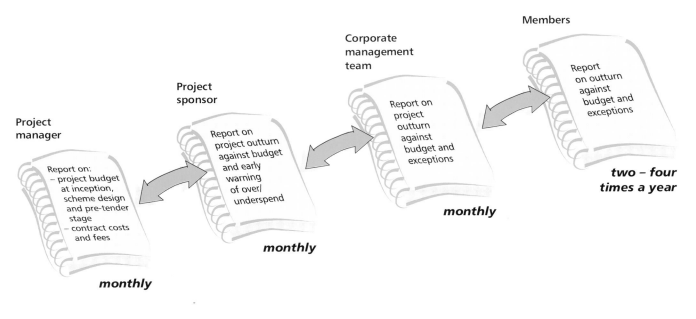

Source: Audit Commission

Corporate management team

- project sponsors report on costs against project budget for each project, but in the context of the authority's overall capital programme;
- reviews reports seeking budget approval at inception, scheme design and at pre-tender stages and considers impact on authority's overall capital programme; and
- monitoring takes place monthly. Exception reports prepared in respect of sensitive, large or complex projects.

Members

- approve project budget at inception, scheme design and pre-tender stages;
- officers report on costs against budget for each project, but in the context of the authority's overall capital programme. Reports produced between two to four times a year; and
- exception reports produced as and when required to resolve issues that could give rise to delays.

6.25 A range of reporting formats were noted during fieldwork. The essential requirements are clarity and an appropriate level of detail. The Metropolitan Borough of Wirral provides an example of presenting essential information well to project managers (Exhibit 6.7).

Exhibit 6.7
Cost report produced by the Metropolitan Borough of Wirral

Essential requirements are clarity and appropriate level of detail.

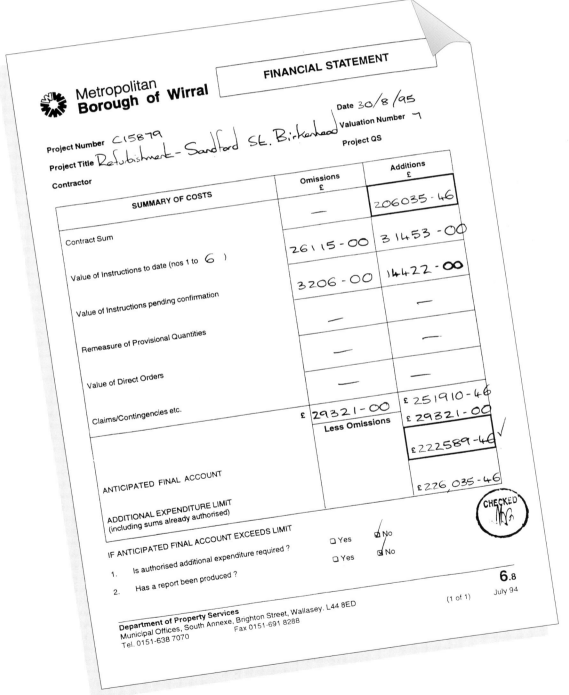

Source: Audit Commission survey

Checklist for action

Aspects of performance	Good practice features	Current practice	Action
Project budgets	Set realistic budgets.		
	Budgets to be prepared by people with appropriate skills.		
	Budgets to be reviewed and updated at key stages (ie, at inception; scheme design; and pre-tender).		
	Use cost-planning techniques.		
	Give design team delegated authority to approve minor variations.		
Cost of technical services	Include cost of technical services in the project budget.		
	Monitor cost of technical services during all stages of the project.		
Monitoring and reporting	Monitor against budget at least monthly.		
	Monitor key cost variables.		
Contingency sums	Include as part of risk assessment.		
	Clear policy for releasing contingency sums.		

7 Risk Management

Risks with potentially damaging consequences are inherent in all construction projects and can arise at any time. They can result in delay and/or additional costs, personal injury or pollution. The objectives of systematic risk management are:

• to identify risks in projects and to assess their significance or potential impact;

• to enable informed and objective responses to be made; and

• to avoid potential loss of time, money or other benefits, and to achieve best value for money.

Risk management involves identifying potential risks systematically and allocating them when the procurement method is chosen. The extent of the risk analysis will depend on the size and complexity of the project, and restrictions placed on it – such as external funding deadlines or self-imposed financial restrictions – which put pressure on the time available for design. Authorities undertake some risk management with varying degrees of effectiveness. Health and safety issues are fairly consistently addressed but preparatory work – such as surveys or ground investigation to reduce design and construction risks – is tackled less systematically. This chapter considers the need for a wider adoption of formal and systematic risk management on larger or more difficult projects, and a more disciplined and deliberate approach to risk management generally. It makes the following key recommendations.

Authorities should:	This will have the following benefits:
◆ implement a systematic approach to risk management which will include the identification of risks, their assessment and options to control them	◆ avoid potential loss of time, money or other benefits, and achieve best value for money
◆ consider risk issues when selecting the procurement method or the form of contract	◆ ensure that the most cost-effective option is selected
◆ provide appropriate contingencies to cover the risks retained by the client	◆ provide better time and cost control and prevent unauthorised changes to the scope of the project once the contract has been let

Principles of risk management

◆ What does a systematic risk management approach involve?

◆ How can risks be identified, assessed, prioritised and controlled?

7.1 Construction, like any other complex activity, involves risks. Construction projects are particularly subject to those which manifest themselves in delays and cost increases. Project risks can also have an impact on health and safety, resulting in personal injury, and on the environment, resulting in pollution. Many authorities set up arbitrary contingencies or provisional sums in contracts as a substitute for the systematic management of risk.

7.2 Risks can also be introduced into projects by funding deadlines, typically putting pressure on the concept and design stages in order to get construction under way. In some cases, deadlines attached to small elements of funding can drive the whole project programme (Case Study 7.1). In others, deadlines are self-imposed. But authorities can minimise the impact of risks by adopting a systematic risk management approach.

Case Study 7.1
A social services project in a county council

Rushing to spend money by the year-end can mean inadequate preparation and higher risk. A pro-active approach to risk management can help minimise the impact of risks.

The Department of Health (DoH) notified the council in June 1994 that it was to be awarded a supplementary credit approval (SCA) of £300,000 as part of the Government's care in the community programme. The money had to be spent by 31 March 1995. As the award was less than half of the council's bid, the social services department had to rethink its original strategy – it set aside £250,000 for a single project to provide a drop-in centre for schizophrenic people in an area of the county that had no current provision. It also decided that new-build was not an option within the timescale. It proceeded to:

- identify a suitable property in the centre of a town;
- negotiate to purchase through the council valuers;
- consult with the local branch of the National Schizophrenia Association, which was to run the centre, on both design and operation;
- engage the in-house building surveyors to draw up plans to renovate and redesign the property, carry out a structural survey and invite tenders for a contractor to carry out the building work;
- seek committee approval for the purchase of the property; and
- seek planning approval for the works and change of use of the property.

All this took time. Getting committee approvals took up two months, as did negotiating the sale of the property.

Project design was rushed and contractors were given a little over two weeks to submit tenders. Two days after the contractor started on site, the district council's building control officer formally reported that the higher floor loading standard required by the change of use would require underfloor investigation before further work could continue. A structural engineer was appointed to investigate the underfloor area. Additional structural work had to be carried out. This put the project more than £20,000 over budget, extended the contract duration from a planned 9 weeks to a total of 17 weeks, and took the work well past the end of the financial year. In the event, the DoH issued a further SCA in 1995/96 which met part of the overrun. The county council had to use £40,000 from its own revenue reserves to complete the project.

The project illustrates several of the problems associated with local authority construction work:

- Targeted, time-limited funding meant that the vital pre-construction phase was rushed.
- Rushed planning and design led to:
  - inadequate preparatory work, so increasing risk;
  - poor cost-estimation; and
  - poor use of the market, by allowing contractors insufficient time to cost bids and setting over-tight contract periods.
- When costs exceeded initial expectations, the tendency was to work with the existing budget ceiling, regardless of the value for money implications of changes.

The authority could have reduced the impact of time-limited funding by taking a more pro-active approach in managing risk. For example, it might have:

- identified alternative strategies in the event that a full award was not made;
- identified the site and obtained committee approval before funding was confirmed;
- tried to obtain earlier access to the building to carry out a survey; and
- started design work before the purchase was completed.

'The formal application of all the processes of systematic risk management carries a cost. It is fully cost-effective only on major or complex projects.'

7.3 None of the fieldwork authorities had implemented a systematic risk management approach. However, they had standard procedures which addressed some well-recognised risks. For example:

◆ financial regulations and standing orders guard against fraud and corruption;

◆ the standard forms of construction contracts provide for insurance to cover risks from injury to persons and property, and other specified hazards;

◆ the basic competence and financial integrity of contractors is covered by the maintenance of an 'approved list' of contractors;

◆ the Construction (Design and Management) Regulations 1994 (CDM Regulations) (Appendix 3) impose obligations on all parties to construction contracts to take steps directed to health and safety on site; and

◆ management procedures standardise practice, and can incorporate useful prompts and checks.

7.4 Authorities undertake some risk management, albeit on a relatively intuitive basis and with varying degrees of success. The issues that are typically addressed are:

◆ health and safety considerations; and

◆ preparatory work, such as surveys or ground investigations to reduce design and construction risk.

7.5 The formal application of all the processes of systematic risk management carries a cost. It is fully cost-effective only on major or complex projects. But the fundamental steps in managing risk (Exhibit 7.1) should always be taken, with a level of detail and formality appropriate to the project (Ref. 15).

Identification of risks

7.6 Unless a risk to the objectives of the project is identified it cannot be consciously managed. The key question 'what can go wrong?' is posed against each of the project objectives. Some answers are provided by experience. But systematic post-project review and keeping of records will greatly facilitate this. A 'what can go wrong' list may be built up on this basis. However, lateral thinking is also required. This may be facilitated by 'brainstorming' within the project team, using as prompts:

◆ the works programme (if available) or other activity lists; and

◆ 'what can go wrong' or other prompt lists.

Exhibit 7.1
Systematic risk management

Risk management can help avoid potential loss of time, money or other benefits and achieve best value for money.

Source: Audit Commission

Assessment of risks

7.7 The risks are assessed by evaluating their potential impact on the project. The impact or severity of the risk is assessed by taking into account:

♦ the likelihood (probability) of the adverse event occurring; and

♦ the consequence (damage) resulting.

Various analytical techniques are available, but for most purposes assessment against qualitative scales is adequate (with *probability* ranging from 'negligible' to 'frequent' and *consequence* ranging from 'negligible' to 'catastrophic'). Combining the two on to a matrix can indicate the impact of the risk, ranging from 'negligible' to 'unacceptable'.

Prioritisation of risks

7.8 Risks are prioritised at an early stage; in the first instance, between those that need managing and those that may be left to chance. If issues are unclear but apparently significant, use of advanced assessment techniques may be required. This allows management resources to be concentrated on the major risks, with the greatest potential for achieving value for money.

Control of risks

7.9 Having identified, assessed and prioritised the risks, action to control them is then considered, in order to reduce their likelihood, their consequences or both (Case Study 7.2, overleaf). In principle, authorities can use a number of options to reduce risk (Box 7A). The risk remaining after this action – 'residual risk' – is kept by the client.

Box 7A
Options for reducing risks

Authorities can use a number of options to reduce risk.

Options available	Examples of possible action
Risk reduction	– further site investigation, whether below ground or of an existing building – alternative method of construction – for example, one which is less prone to weather conditions – implementing a checking procedure to detect design faults
Risk transfer passing ownership of the risk to another party	– under 'design and build' arrangement, risks related to the delivery of information to meet the needs of construction on site pass to the contractor – insuring against the risk
Risk avoidance	– writing an exception clause into a contract, to allow the reappraisal, replacement or cancellation of a project if the risk consequences are unacceptable
Risk removal removing a hazard from a project so that it no longer poses a threat	– preliminary contract to locate and remove asbestos
Risk sharing the risk exposure is beyond the capacity of one party, and a realistic way of sharing it can be agreed	– joint venture arrangement – private finance initiative

Case Study 7.2
Risk management assessment undertaken by Devon County Council

Careful research at the start of a project will help to minimise the risk of a project failing to meet service needs.

The service risks (and the underlying need for a major project at a community college) were tested by:

◆ analysing general population trends;

◆ undertaking a local population survey (including interviewing local GPs);

◆ examining predictions in the local housing market (including interviewing estate agents and developers);

◆ analysis of all the education services in the area; and

◆ identifying current and proposed curriculum requirements and testing these against current and planned provision with full involvement of college staff.

The existing facilities were also tested by:

◆ undertaking a comprehensive condition survey;

◆ auditing the existing facilities against the authority standards; and

◆ drilling boreholes to test ground conditions.

Construction work was carried out over 94 weeks while the college was still operational. Measures taken to address associated risks of danger and disruption included:

◆ building a temporary road on to the site so that construction traffic was separated from pupils; and

◆ producing a very detailed programme, as part of the tender documentation, setting out the order of work, phasing, access ways to be kept open and communication methods, with the full involvement of the school staff.

The project was considered very successful by the council, by the contractor, and by the college – which was at no time prevented from carrying out its planned business.

Not all risks can be predicted. Government policy to expand General National and Vocational Qualifications (GNVQ) was announced during the project and sixth-form facilities at the college are now more crowded than originally envisaged.

The practice of risk management

◆ Who is responsible for risk management and how it is applied?

7.10 The practice of systematic risk management within a project is normally the responsibility of a risk management team assembled for the purpose. It will include senior members of the client organisation and design team with responsibility for the project, together with a facilitator who may be an existing member of the team or externally appointed. The facilitator leads the process; in particular, convening and chairing meetings. Members of the team are selected for their ability to identify risks and strategies to control them.

7.11 Systematic risk management is planned ahead from inception and expressed in a 'risk management plan' which is a key component of the project execution plan. Sections of the execution plan will cover such aspects as:

◆ scope of risk management;

◆ risk management methods;

◆ activities;

◆ project programme;

◆ confidentiality; and

◆ deliverables.

7.12 The risk register is a commonly used means of recording and controlling the process of systematic risk management. It always includes descriptions of the risks that have been identified and a record of action taken to reduce them. Depending on the project and the demand for risk management it may also:

- subdivide risks into more detail;
- provide a measure of probability and consequences;
- identify ownership of risks;
- record importance/cost/acceptability of risks;
- state capability for/cost of/ownership of mitigating actions;
- give timings of actions;
- assess residual risks; and
- record changes in importance/cost/acceptability of risk.

7.13 Box 7B provides a checklist which authorities can use to identify the issues that they need to consider.

Box 7B
Risk management

Key questions

	Yes	No	Issues for consideration
1. Do we have a systematic approach to risk management for each project?	☐	☐	
2. Is the approach appropriate to the size and complexity of each project/type of projects?	☐	☐	
3. Do we always identify the possible risks to project objectives?	☐	☐	
4. Do we evaluate the impact of the risks that we identify?	☐	☐	
5. Do we take action to reduce the risks that we identify?	☐	☐	
6. Do we identify all the risks that manifest themselves during all stages (from inception to handover) of projects?	☐	☐	
7. Do we recognise threats from 'external pressures' such as conditions attached to funding approvals?	☐	☐	
8. Do we have the right environment to support good project management? (do we have the right design team? is the client function clearly allocated and effectively discharged? are briefs clear? are project programmes realistic? are project budgets adequate? do we have effective monitoring and reporting arrangements?)	☐	☐	

Selection of procurement option

- Do we take into account risk implications when we select our procurement approach?
- How do we provide for contingencies and how do we control them?

7.14 Fieldwork authorities selected their procurement approach (Chapter 4) on the basis of:

- the need for accountability;
- both the legal and technical departments', and the local builders', familiarity with commonly used forms of contract; and
- the need for speed to achieve deadlines.

7.15 Risk implications did not appear to be a major consideration, and if they were, the authority's objective was fairly typically to shed risk. However, a strategy that seeks to shed *all* risk on to those contracted to the authority is unlikely to be effective. Under normal trading conditions, tenderers will place a premium on risk. The greater the uncertainty, the higher the premium. In practice, firms bidding on tight margins will seek to pass back to the client the cost of risk, and the forms of contract will not necessarily provide a safeguard.

7.16 A wide range of options is available for the allocation of risk under the various forms of contract. As an example, two extremes are possible in a traditional procurement context in allocating risk relating to the cost of construction:

- a *fixed-price, lump-sum* contract requires the firm entering the contract to accept all the risks in completing the contract within the quoted sum. However, the client still retains the risk of the contractor either failing to perform or of seeking means of passing back the cost of risk. In a fixed-price contract, the client will also have no flexibility regarding changes to the contract; and
- a *cost-plus* form of contract places nearly all the risk on the client, but does afford the client considerable flexibility in approach.

7.17 The management of risk should be a primary consideration when considering the procurement system and form of contract to be used (Chapter 4). In principle, the issues are the same for the procurement of technical services and for construction.

Contingency planning

7.18 It is essential to provide appropriate contingencies to cover the risks retained by the client, including residual risk. These contingencies may be in the form of:

- tolerance in the specification (quality);
- float in the programme (time); and
- money in the budget (cost).

7.19 These elements have to be balanced. However, while authorities generally provide no tolerance in specification or flexibility in deadline, many provide a financial contingency. Decisions as to the size of the contingency and where it is held require judgement in the light of project circumstances. It may be included in the authority's capital programme or in the project budget. In the latter case it must be clear what the contingency is for and who has authority to spend it.

'The management of risk should be a primary consideration when considering the procurement system and form of contract to be used.'

7.20 Authority to spend part or all of the contingency provision in the contract sum can give the design team some flexibility in responding to events. If the contingency is kept within the capital programme, the design team will need to get specific authority for any additional expenditure. In practice, the capital programme in some authorities includes a 'negative contingency' by way of a projected over-spend, to ensure that the full allocation is spent within the financial year. Other authorities build a degree of flexibility into their capital programmes in order to bring forward or defer projects to match expenditure targets.

7.21 Many authorities provide a contingency in the form of a contingency sum and/or provisional sums in contracts. The Commission's survey of 700 contracts shows that 95 per cent of contracts included such contingencies. But there was a wide range in the level of provision made which tends to suggest that contingencies are not set on the basis of a rigorous assessment of risk (Table 7.1). Furthermore, contingencies are sometimes provided as an alternative to good planning and design (Chapters 3, 5 and 6)

Table 7.1
Contingencies/provisional sums as a percentage of contract sum

Contingency/provisional sums vary significantly. Sums are used as an alternative to planning and good design.

Source: Audit Commission survey

Type of contract	Contract sum	Min. %	Lower quartile %	Median %	Average %	Upper quartile %	Max. %
New-build	less than £100,000	0.00	3.19	5.32	7.68	9.47	31.57
	more than £100,000	0.00	4.58	7.63	9.45	11.16	51.11
	more than £500,000	0.00	3.11	6.23	7.24	9.34	20.10
Renovation	less than £100,000	0.00	4.64	8.36	11.25	12.73	71.18
	more than £100,000	0.00	4.50	7.64	11.72	13.80	64.83
	more than £500,000	0.00	6.38	9.55	14.38	17.44	54.45
Mechanical and engineering	less than £100,000	0.00	3.93	6.95	8.94	10.76	53.46
	more than £100,000	0.00	3.21	4.66	6.77	8.97	25.13
External works	less than £100,000	0.00	4.44	7.30	8.30	10.33	35.48
	more than £100,000	4.17	8.50	12.95	13.31	14.07	37.30
	more than £500,000	0.00	3.70	9.73	7.84	12.25	13.50

Checklist for action

	Good practice features	Current practice	Action
Systematic risk management	Identify, assess and prioritise risks, and take action to control them.		
	Tailor procedures to type and size of project.		
	Maintain and use risk register.		
	Identify responsibility for risk management clearly and allocate.		
Choice of procurement method	Client decides how much risk to accept and plans procurement strategy accordingly.		
Contingency planning	Base provision for contingencies on the level of both retained and residual risks.		
	Control release of contingencies.		

Quality management procedures ensure that projects achieve set objectives – in particular, in the quality of specification, design and construction. These procedures include:

- a selection process to appoint the right project team;

- quality planning in which project objectives are defined and a framework established for quality control;

- the exercise of quality control during design and construction; and

- post-project review to continue improvement in performance.

8 Quality Management

Authorities generally recognise and understand the need to control the quality of construction work. The appointment of clerks of works or other means of inspecting work in progress are fairly typical. But authorities could improve their performance by adopting a more systematic approach to the management of quality during the design and construction processes, and by appointing the right team for each project. This chapter considers these issues and makes the following recommendations.

Authorities should:	*This will have the following benefits:*
◆ define their quality objectives and implement a framework for quality control during design and construction	◆ ensures that quality is maintained throughout the process, and minimises the risk of error due to: – oversight of critical item; – staff changes; or – lack of familiarity with procedures
◆ appoint the team on the basis of quality as well as cost	◆ makes appropriate skills available to deliver successful projects
◆ carry out post-project reviews	◆ improves performance by learning from both successes and failures, and provides better accountability

Quality management system

◆ Do we have a clear and agreed approach for delivering projects to the quality of design, specification and construction that we require?

8.1 The purpose of quality management is to ensure that a project achieves its set objectives, in particular in realising a quality of design, specification and construction that is appropriate to the client's needs. Effective quality management must address the procedures for carrying out projects as well as the quality of the product which is finally delivered.

8.2 Authorities generally control the quality of the physical end-product, particularly during construction on site. The employment of a clerk of works or other means of inspecting work in progress is fairly typical. However, the quality of design and construction processes is not addressed in a systematic way by most authorities.

8.3 The quality of a production process can be controlled by a formal quality management system (QMS); that is, a set of documented procedures designed to ensure that the process *consistently* delivers the required quality. Authorities may have their QMS externally assessed as conforming to ISO9000 (formerly BS5750) by an authorised accreditation body, and thereby be registered ('certified') as 'quality assessed'. The Audit Commission's fieldwork found only one authority where the in-house technical services department had achieved certification to ISO9000. However, other authorities had introduced similar, highly documented procedures that imposed discipline on the project management process, minimising errors and building quality checks into the process.

The failure to apply a quality management system may result in costly late changes.

At a fieldwork authority which did not have a quality management system, the design team responsible for a £700,000 housing renovation project failed to consider at the design stage whether they needed to get planning approval. At the tender stage they approached the planning officer. The design team had to make late changes which resulted in increased costs. Other projects in the programme also had to be delayed.

8.4 Quality management systems do have a price in terms of additional time taken for certain tasks and thus in general overhead costs. Set against this, however, is the confidence of authorities that their systems are robust and relatively secure against staff changes. The cost of not having systems can also be high (Case Study 8.1).

8.5 Some authorities operate much more informally and are still equally effective. But this mode of operation is highly dependent on a teamwork culture, the contribution of key personalities and the extent to which the range of work is familiar to project teams. These authorities may also be vulnerable when key members of the team leave.

8.6 The remainder of this chapter examines the key aspects of an effective quality management system (Exhibit 8.1):

◆ *quality planning* – in which objectives are defined and a framework for quality control is established;

◆ *quality control exercised during the design and construction stages* of a project; and

◆ *post-project review* – undertaken as part of a continuous improvement programme.

Exhibit 8.1
Quality management

Effective quality management results in continuous improvement in performance.

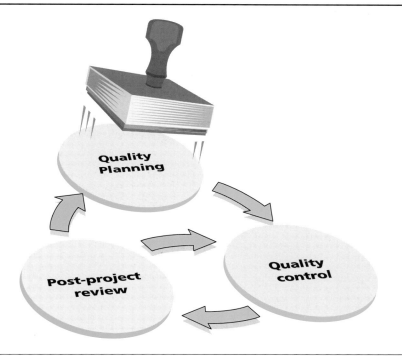

Source: Audit Commission

Quality planning

◆ How effectively do we apply quality management to each project?

8.7 To be fully effective, quality management needs to be set in the context of an overall quality policy adopted by authorities and planned from inception on a project-by-project basis, by means of a project quality plan. The formality of the quality management policy and procedures will depend on authorities' circumstances, and the size and nature of projects. All arrangements should be documented to make sure that they are robust, well understood and consistently applied.

8.8 Although authorities recognise the importance of quality issues, their approach to quality management generally relies on the experience and skill of their design team. Such an approach exposes authorities to a greater level of risk because key tasks may be overlooked as the result of staff changes, a lack of familiarity with procedures or inadequate planning time. One fieldwork authority followed good practice by requiring the production of a 'project quality plan' for each project (Case Study 8.2). The formality and detail of the project quality plan will depend on the project, but the essential requirements are that it:

◆ lists the procedures for quality planning;

◆ allocates responsibility (Chapter 2 – Roles and Responsibilities);

◆ provides a checking mechanism which prevents key tasks being overlooked (Exhibit 8.2); and

◆ delivers the level of quality that is appropriate to the client's needs and objectives within budget (Case Study 8.3 [overleaf] and Chapter 3 – Value Management and Value Engineering).

Case Study 8.2
Wirral Metropolitan Borough
Council's quality procedures

Quality plans help to minimise the risk of errors.

The 'project quality plan' consists of general procedures that set out the framework within which the (technical) project officer designs and supervises a project plan from inception to completion. The plan covers:

◆ investigation of site conditions, ownership and other preliminary issues;

◆ appointment of technical disciplines;

◆ design team meetings and liaison;

◆ design reviews;

◆ tendering; and

◆ contract administration.

The procedures are supported by a series of standard forms and a project-specific checklist, signed off as issues are dealt with.

Exhibit 8.2
Quality plan produced by the Metropolitan Borough of Wirral

The quality plan provides a checking mechanism that prevents key tasks being overlooked.

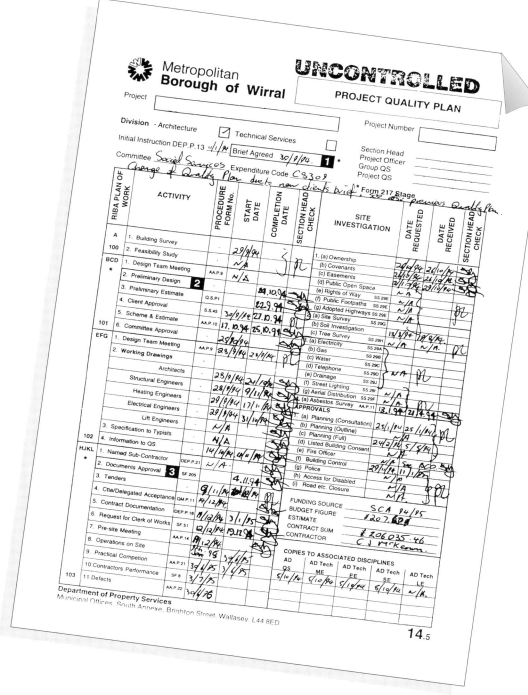

Source: Department of Property Services, Wirral Metropolitan Borough Council

---

Quality levels specified for the development were carefully considered, to match the objectives of the authority as client, and required:

♦ good standard aesthetically for finishes and landscaping to attract the desired types of tenant;

♦ robust specifications where necessary to withstand heavy use (for example, brickwork to lower elevations rather than profiled cladding); and

♦ good quality materials and design generally to reduce maintenance costs (the authority would be the landlord).

The authority's approach was supported by feedback from tenants of older units who were willing to pay higher rents for better quality accommodation.

Quality control during design

♦ Do we have effective procedures that enable us to control quality during design?

8.9 The primary objective of controlling quality during the design process is to ensure that the design meets the client's needs and objectives, as expressed in the project brief (Chapter 3). A number of fieldwork authorities included design reviews at milestone points in the design process, when the design was checked by a person outside the immediate project design team. Other authorities relied on the skill, experience and judgement of their technical staff, but with less visible assurance of the quality of the design.

8.10 For large and complex projects, particularly those that are unusual or one-offs, client/user representatives should be involved in the design reviews and sign off drawings and specifications when approved. This is particularly important in joint venture arrangements, or when building for a known leaseholder, to avoid any subsequent dispute regarding the extent and quality of work.

8.11 The quality of the documentation used to convey the intentions and requirements of the design to the contractor must also be controlled. Fieldwork did not show significant problems in this area, but in the construction industry inadequate information is the reason most frequently given for 'claims' submitted by contractors for extensions of time or reimbursement of 'loss and expense' (Chapters 5 and 6).

Assembling the right team

♦ How well do we put together our design team?

8.12 Whatever the formality of the checking procedure, the need for a professionally skilled design team is paramount. It is essential that:

♦ the performance of in-house technical services is monitored; and that

♦ external consultants are selected with reference to quality of service (Chapter 4 – Selection of Consultants). Certification to ISO9000 standard indicates a commitment to quality, but should not be the only criterion by which quality is assessed.

If the project so demands, external expertise should be brought in from the earliest stages (Case Study 8.4).

Appropriate use of external expertise during design can help deliver value for money.

In developing the design brief for a sports centre, the authority relied heavily on advice from the Technical Unit at the Sports Council, as well as consulting with local sports clubs. Similarly, the design paid close attention to operational aspects, making further use of technical advice from the Sports Council. For example:

- doors opening outwards from the main hall;
- ventilation arranged not to disturb badminton shuttlecocks;
- adequate storage for equipment;
- selection of sports flooring; and
- calculation of changing accommodation requirements.

Quality control during construction

- How effective are our quality control arrangements during construction?

8.13 The primary objective of quality control during construction is to ensure full conformity with the drawings and specifications and an appropriate standard of workmanship. Again, the paramount requirement is to have the right people on the job, and this was a conscious objective at a number of fieldwork authorities.

8.14 Contractors should always be invited to tender on the basis of their willingness and ability to deliver the quality required. A significant number of contractors employed by the fieldwork authorities were certified to ISO9000, and others had their own QMS in operation on the contract. As with consultants, certification demonstrates a commitment to quality, but should not be the sole criterion for selection.

8.15 The concept of each firm taking responsibility for the quality of its own output is fundamental to the operation of a QMS on the ISO9000 model. However, a clerk of works (CoW) was appointed to the majority of projects that were reviewed during fieldwork, irrespective of the contractor being ISO9000-registered. In fact, contractors generally welcomed the appointment of a CoW, provided the atmosphere was one of teamwork. In cases where a CoW was not appointed, inspection was undertaken by a member of the design team.

Post-project review

- Do we systematically review projects with a view to improving performance across the authority?

8.16 Fieldwork authorities have learned from past experience, adopting standards and specifications that have been seen to have worked well. Authorities also used knowledge gained on early contracts in a series to make improvements to the later contracts. However, there was little evidence of systematic post-project review. As a consequence, authorities are missing a significant opportunity to gain from their accumulated knowledge. Systematic reviews (Box 8A, overleaf) help to:

- assess outcomes against project objectives;
- inform design approaches and standards for future use;
- lead to improvements in procurement and other procedures;
- raise performance generally, by building up, in effect, a series of internally generated benchmarks; and
- refine a standing select list of contractors and consultants.

Box 8A
Post-project review

Post-project review
Project.................................

Key questions	Yes	No	What improvements do we need to make?
Organisation management (Chapter 2)			
1. Were systems and procedures appropriate to the specific needs of the project?	❏	❏	
2. Did we clearly define the roles and responsibilities of the project team?	❏	❏	
3. Did the client have the necessary skills to draw up a brief and to manage the project?	❏	❏	
4. Were technical resources planned and were they appropriate for the project?	❏	❏	
5. Is there evidence of effective teamworking?	❏	❏	
6. Did we communicate effectively with all stakeholders?	❏	❏	
7. Are users satisfied with the project?	❏	❏	
Option and design management (Chapter 3)			
7. Was the need/objective for the project identified, recorded, agreed and approved?	❏	❏	
8. Was the project brief signed off by the project sponsor before design work started?	❏	❏	
9. Were changes made after the contractor started on site?	❏	❏	
10. Did we apply value management or value engineering techniques?	❏	❏	
Procurement management (Chapter 4)	❏	❏	
11. Was the procurement option chosen after an evaluation of risk?	❏	❏	
12. Was the need for professional services identified when the project was approved?	❏	❏	
13. Did we follow good practice: – in appointing consultants? – in selecting and appointing contractors?	❏	❏	
Cost management (Chapter 5)			
14. Was the difference between the successful tender sum and the approved budget less than 15 per cent?	❏	❏	
15. Did the project budget include professional fees?	❏	❏	
16. Did the design team use cost-planning techniques?	❏	❏	

Box 8A (cont.)

Key questions	Yes	No	What improvements do we need to make?
17. Was the difference between the final cost and the contract sum less than 5 per cent?	❏	❏	
18. Were costs monitored during construction and reported to the client?	❏	❏	
19. Did the client approve all significant variations?	❏	❏	
Time management (Chapter 6)			
20. Was a project timetable which identified key stages drawn up and agreed?	❏	❏	
21. Was performance against the timetable monitored?	❏	❏	
22. Were significant variations reported to the client?	❏	❏	
23. Was action taken in response to slippage?	❏	❏	
Risk management (Chapter 7)			
24. Were risks to and from the project identified from the outset?	❏	❏	
25. Were the risks assessed and action taken to allocate or manage them?	❏	❏	
Quality management (Chapter 8)			
26. Was our quality management system appropriate to the project?	❏	❏	
27. Did the quality of design and construction meet the standards we expected?	❏	❏	

Checklist for action

Aspects of performance	Good practice features	Current practice	Action
Defining quality objectives	Client's needs/objectives should be clearly stated for each project.		
	Establish level of quality that meets client's needs/objectives for each project.		
Framework for quality	Authority should adopt quality policy.		
control during design and construction	Put quality management system in operation.		
	Produce quality project plan for each project.		
	Design reviews at project milestones should be carried out by a person independent of the design team.		
	Check completeness and quality of design information before handover to contractor.		
	Appoint clerk of works to oversee construction.		
Appointing the team	Monitor the performance of in-house technical staff.		
	Appoint consultants on the basis of quality as well as price.		
	Appoint contractors who can demonstrate that they have systematic quality management procedures.		
Post-project reviews	Ensure systematic review of completed projects as part of an authority-wide, continuous improvement programme.		

Appendix 1

Construction Industry Board Reports

The Construction Industry Board (CIB) provides guidance for the development of the construction industry by improving efficiency and effectiveness throughout the construction procurement process. The CIB's objectives are to implement, maintain, monitor and review the recommendations in the Latham Report (Ref. 2). In August 1994 the members of the CIB set up a number of working groups to take forward recommendations outlined in the Latham Report.

The working groups have produced thirteen guides as follows:

Briefing the team	This guide defines the briefing process, examines the factors affecting the quality of briefing and considers the criteria by which good briefing can be judged. It also reviews the guidance already available and considers what further guidance is needed for both public and private sector clients.
Constructing success	This code of practice assists clients in acquiring their desired end product and obtaining value for money. It is a statement of best practice but is aimed at the lay person.
Code of practice for the selection of subcontractors	This code of practice sets out the following key principles. It: – seeks a commitment to short tender lists and selection on the basis of quality and price; – ensures that contractors offer subcontractors which meet the principles contained in the Latham Report; – rules out *Dutch* auctioning; – ensures that main contractors notify clients, before starting work, of the names of subcontractors; and – secures a commitment from subcontractors to work co-operatively with other subcontractors.
Selecting consultants for the team: balancing quality and price	This report endorses a specific quality and price assessment mechanism for the appointment of professional consultants (Ref. 9).
Framework for a national register for consultants	This report considers the issues relating to the creation of a single register of consultants

seeking public sector work and the appropriate requirements for entry to the register.

Framework for a national register for contractors	This report develops a standard pre-qualification form for public sector work. It considers the issues relating to the creation of a single register of contractors seeking public sector work, and the appropriate requirements for entry on that register.
Training the team	The report identifies the action government and industry need to take to implement the Latham Report recommendations on training.
Constructing a better image	This report recommends how the construction industry can improve its image and investment encouraged. It establishes achievement targets and sets out key milestones to measure performance and progress.
Tomorrow's team: women and men in construction	This report focuses on equal opportunities for women within the construction industry. It encourages the development of attitudes, practices and physical environments within the industry that do not have the effect of placing women at a disadvantage.
Educating the professional team	This report sets out the organisational and financial structures to co-ordinate the education of construction professionals.
Liability law and latent defects insurance	This report sets out the provisions which government needs to include in a construction contracts bill.
Towards a 30 per cent productivity improvement in construction	This report identifies and promotes a means of achieving a 30 per cent real cost reduction by the year 2000 across the construction industry as a whole. It promotes value for money and quality management as a means of improving competitiveness. It also makes proposals on benchmarking.
Partnering in the team	This report promotes the practice of partnering where appropriate in both the private and public sectors by establishing best practice benchmarks, facilitating the dissemination of good practice, and ensuring the development of appropriate training and education packages.

Appendix 2

The Housing Grants, Construction and Regeneration Act 1996

The Housing Grants, Construction and Regeneration Act 1996 (the Act) received Royal Assent in July 1996. Part 2 of the Act provides a framework for fairer contracts and better working relationships within the construction industry. It specifies that construction contracts must contain certain provisions relating to adjudication and payment, and that – where they do not – parties may rely upon fall-back provisions as contained in regulations made by the Secretary of State. The regulations will be known as *The Scheme for Construction Contracts* (the Scheme).

The Department of the Environment (DoE) has consulted widely on its proposals for the Scheme. When the DoE has considered all responses it will draft a statutory instrument to implement the Scheme. Once the Scheme has been approved by Parliament – probably in mid 1997 – the Secretary of State will be able to make an order to put into effect the whole of Part 2 of the Act.

How the Scheme will work

The Scheme will have two sections: Part 1 of the Scheme dealing with adjudication and Part 2 dealing with payments.

As far as adjudication is concerned, unless a contract contains an adjudication agreement which satisfies all the requirements of section 108 of the Act, then any party to that contract who wishes to pursue adjudication must invoke Part 1 of the Scheme in its entirety.

Part 2 of the Scheme covers payments timetables, certification of the amount due for payment and final payments. For many contracts it will not be necessary to import all the provisions of Part 2 of the Scheme *en bloc*. Instead, parties may draw upon it piecemeal as indicated by the Act.

Appendix 3

The Construction (Design and Management) Regulations 1994

The Construction (Design and Management) Regulations (CDM) apply to all building and civil engineering projects and fitting out, repair and maintenance works (including redecoration and cleaning), other than those defined as small. 'Small' implies works which last no more than 30 days or which do not involve more than 500 person days of construction work. Other construction exceptions include off-site fabrication or work for domestic clients, where design requirements only apply. However, all demolition or dismantling works fall within the remit of CDM.

The primary purpose of the regulations is to establish a safety management network, plan and file, in order to reduce potential hazards in design and on sites. Identified hazards should either be designed out or, if residual, appropriate precautions introduced as the project moves into its construction phase. There are no technical requirements to be satisfied or approvals to be sought. Project particulars must be notified to local Health and Safety Executive Offices (H&SE).

The regulations are statutory and enforcement lies with the H&SE. It has powers to issue improvement and prohibition notices, to pursue criminal prosecutions and seek fines of up to £5,000 in magistrates courts, with more serious cases being referred to the crown courts for unlimited fines and/or imprisonment.

A 'planning supervisor' and a 'principal contractor' must be appointed as early as practicable in the design/procurement process. Both must have been selected on the basis of competence, expertise and resource.

The planning supervisor is responsible for:

◆ all project notifications to the local authority or H&SE office;

◆ advising the client on the competence and capability of designers and contractors to fulfil their duties under the regulations;

◆ producing, developing and maintaining a project health and safety plan (HSP) and the 'owners' manual' file (HSF) throughout the life of the project;

◆ providing a copy of the HSP for each contractor and subcontractor before they start work on site;

◆ reviewing and co-ordinating contributions from all 'designers' and 'constructors' to eliminate health and safety risks; and

◆ ensuring that the final HSF also includes provision for subsequent maintenance of the building through to demolition and that the HSF is delivered safely to the client.

The planning supervisor joins the design team as an expert on health and safety (H&S) matters, acting in an H&S co-ordinating role between other members of the design team. It is necessary for the planning supervisor to be appointed very early in the life of a project.

All other members of the design team who produce drawings or documentation associated with procuring projects are viewed as 'designers' (or CDM duty holders). They are required to assure the planning supervisor that they have sufficient knowledge, competence and resources to make a positive contribution to the health and safety plan.

The principal contractor is almost always likely to be the main contractor. Once appointed, he will add information to the HSP to reflect his and his subcontractors' organisations and working practices. He will also take responsibility for the construction element of the plan and for co-ordinating and, if necessary, imposing safety rules on other contractors on site. It should be noted that these regulations complement a contractor's existing duties under the Health and Safety at Work Act 1974, rather than replacing them.

Appendix 4

Standard Forms of Building Contract

A number of standard forms of contract for construction work are available; those most likely to be applied in a local authority context are listed below, according to publisher. The list is not comprehensive. The dates quoted are when the current edition was first published.

Joint Contracts Tribunal (JCT)

Standard form of building contract 1980 edition (JCT 80)

This is one of the most widely used forms for traditional designer-led building contracts. It is available with or without quantities, for use where full information is available at the time of tendering, or with approximate quantities. Time is an essential part of the contract. The contract is administered by either an architect or contract administrator. Specific and detailed provisions are made for nominating subcontractors and suppliers who are required to enter into complementary standard subcontracts. These include a warranty for design and performance direct to the client.

Supplements exist to extend its scope for sectional completion, allowing phasing of the works and for introducing an element of contractor's (builder's) design. Separate editions are available for local authority and private use.

Contractors' designed portion supplement 1981 edition

This supplement may be used for adapting the JCT80 standard form, both private and local authorities versions, where the contractor is required to complete the design of part of the works (the 'contractors' designed portion').

Agreement for minor building works 1980 edition (MW80)

This is a straightforward, fixed-price, lump-sum contract for small and simple traditional projects of short duration. It is not available for use with quantities but can be scheduled and priced to afford a degree of cost control. Time is an essential part of the contract. The contract is administered by the architect/supervising officer. No supplements are available to extend the range of the contract, neither is there provision for nominated subcontract arrangements.

Intermediate form of building contract for works of simple content 1984 edition (IFC84)

A mid-range, lump-sum contract designed to be used for relatively simple traditional projects without complex service installations. It may be used by either public or private sectors, with or without quantities, but the job must be fully designed at tender stage. The contract is administered either by an architect or contract administrator. Time is an essential part of the contract and should not exceed 12 months. Subcontractors may be named, but not nominated. Supplements exist to allow for sectional completion.

Standard form of building contract with contractor's design 1981 edition (WCD81)

This form is intended for use where the builder takes full responsibility for the design, but allows flexibility in who actually undertakes design. Care needs to be taken in defining the responsibility where the client has a substantial input. Time is essential to the contract. The contract gives right of access to the employer's agent, but makes no provision of supervision for the quality of the works.

Standard form of prime cost contract 1992 (PCC92)

For work to be carried out on a cost reimbursement basis, with a fixed or percentage fee for the builders' overheads and profit. Nomination of subcontractors is possible.

Association of Consultant Architects

The ACA form of building agreement 1982 – second edition 1984 (ACA Form)

A lump-sum contract intended for any size or type of project, though probably best suited to middle-range jobs. In the private or public sectors it is not as widely used as the JCT contracts. It may be used with or without quantities and is capable of considerable flexibility through the use of option clauses. These allow for both the traditional designer-led arrangements and for the builder to take some responsibility for design. They also provide for more detailed conditions with respect to time.

Architects and Surveyors Institute (ASI)

The ASI (formed by the amalgamation of the Faculty of Architects and Surveyors and the Construction Surveyors Institute) publishes standard forms for traditional designer-led projects used largely by its own members.

ASI minor works contract (1980)

Intended for very small works. A fixed-price contract based upon drawings and specifications. There is no provision for quantities.

ASI small works contract (1981)

Fixed-price or fluctuating, lump-sum contract which can be extended by supplementary conditions to be used with quantities. No provisions for nomination.

ASI building contract (1986)

Intended for larger or more complex work. A lump-sum contract which may be used with or without quantities. Provision for nominating subcontractors and suppliers.

Institution of Civil Engineers (ICE)

The ICE conditions of contract – sixth edition 1991

This is the major form for use with civil engineering works and is based on tender drawings, specification and estimated quantities. The work is subject to remeasurement as it proceeds. Time is an essential part of the contract, which is administered by the engineer. Only available in approximate quantities form.

The ICE conditions of contract for minor works first edition 1988 (ICE minor works form)

A straightforward contract for small civil engineering works of short duration. Can be used with quantities but more usually where re-measurement is anticipated.

Conditions of contract for design and construct 1992

The standard form for design-and-build projects of a civil engineering nature, it replaces the role of the independent 'engineer' with that of 'employer's representative' who acts on behalf of the client. There is no provision for a 'resident engineer' to act as inspector. It includes compulsory conciliation procedures.

Engineering and construction contract (ECC) – formerly the new engineering contract (NEC)

The ECC is intended to facilitate good management by motivating each of the participants to manage their own contribution. It claimed to be sufficiently flexible for use in:

- projects involving any combination of engineering and construction disciplines;
- large and small projects;
- traditional or management-based procurement arrangements;
- contracts with or without bills of quantities;
- contracts with design carried out by the contractor in part, entirely or not at all;
- contracts with the proportion of work subcontracted from zero to 100 per cent; and
- cost reimbursement and target cost contracts.

Experience of the ECC to date is limited and generally confined to a small number of major clients.

TBV Consult

PSA/1 with quantities June 1994

This form was developed from GC/Works/1 Edition 3, for building and civil engineering projects in both private and public sectors. It is for use with bills of quantities, where all or most of the quantities are firm, giving a lump-sum contract subject to adjustment for variations ordered. It provides for:

- payment according to stage payment chart and programme;
- pre-agreement of prices and variations;
- defined single-point responsibility of the project manager; and
- specification of the desired level of design ability.

PSA/1 contains all ancillary documents usually needed, such as collateral warranties and performance bonds.

No experience in its use has been built up.

Appendix 5

RIBA Work Stages

Stage		Activity
A	Inception	– Prepare general outline of requirements.
		– Set up client organisation, appoint technical team.
B	Feasibility	– Studies of user requirements, site conditions, etc.
		– Provide client with appraisal of feasibility, to enable form of project to be determined.
C	Outline proposals	– Develop brief.
		– Carry out further studies of user requirements, technical problems, etc
		– Determine general layout, design and construction.
D	Scheme design	– Complete brief.
		– Complete design to point at which size, spatial arrangements, character and cost can be agreed with client.
E	Detail design	– Complete design to point at which all issues of design, specification, construction and cost can be agreed with client.
F	Production information	– Prepare drawings, schedules, specifications to which job will be built.
		– Obtain specialist quotations/agree prime cost sums/place advance orders.
G	Bills of quantities	– Prepare bills of quantities, tender documents.
H	Tender action	– Administer tender procedures, accept tender.
J	Project planning	– Agree construction programme, make contract arrangements.
K	Operations on site	– Hand over site to contractor .
		– Administer contract.
L	Completion	– Practical completion, handover.
		– Commissioning.
		– Agree final account with contractor.
M	Feedback	– Post-project review.

Glossary

As-built drawings   Drawings provided for the building owner recording how the project was *actually* constructed.

Bill of quantities   Contract document listing items of work measured according to a 'standard method of measurement', used in compiling the tender bids and as a basis for pricing variations.

Briefing   The process that enbles the client to identify and agree with the design team the objectives, scope and detailed requirements for the project.

Building surveyor   A person trained in building construction and law, frequently the leader of the design team on refurbishment or renewal works.

CDM Regulations   Construction (Design and Management) Regulations 1994 (see Appendix 3).

Claim   Not a formal contract term, but commonly applied to a request by the contractor for an extension of time or additional payment under the contract, in particular for 'additional loss and expense'.

Clerk of works   Undertakes day-to-day supervision of construction on behalf of the client, usually reporting to the Contract Administrator.

Client   Normally a service committee working through a relevant department – the client is responsible for procuring construction works, paying for and owning the completed assets (See Chapter 2 – Box 2A).

Client team   See Chapter 2 – Box 2A.

Construction adviser   Appointed by the project sponsor to provide professional advice. See Chapter 2 – Box 2A.

Construction management   See Chapter 4 – Box 4A.

Construction period   The actual period of construction from the date works start on site to the date of the certificate of practical completion.

Construction team   See Chapter 2 – Box 2A.

Contingency sum   A sum of money included in the contract sum for paying for unforeseen items.

Contract administrator	The term used in the JCT Standard Forms of Contract for the person who supervises the construction works on behalf of the client, and who is empowered to issue instructions and certificates under the contract. The person is usually the design team leader.
Contract completion date	The date specified in the contract documents for the completion of works.
Contract start date	The date referred to in the contract documents for the contractor's possession of the site.
Contract period	The period between the contract start date and the contract completion date.
Contract sum	The sum in the contract as the total payable for the works described in the contract documents.
Cost consultant	Usually a quantity surveyor (see Chapter 2 – Box 2A).
Cost planning	Costs are systematically analysed and planned during the design stages of a project (see Chapter 6).
Cost reports	Regular reports (usually produced by cost consultants) setting out the financial position of a project.
Co-ordinated project information (CPI)	A systematic way of arranging and presenting design information.
Defects liability period	A period of time after practical completion stated in the contract documents during which the contractor remains responsible for remedying building defects.
Design and build	See Chapter 4 – Box 4A.
Design stages	Recognised stages into which the design process is commonly divided. Those most commonly referred to are those suggested by the Royal Institute of British Architects (RIBA) – see Appendix 6.
Design team	See Chapter 2 – Box 2A.
Design team leader	The person with responsibility for co-ordinating the work of the design team (See Chapter 2 – Box 2A).
Detailed design	The design stage when the design is developed into detailed information to be used by the contractor for construction.

Domestic subcontractor	A subcontractor who has been selected by and is the responsibility of the contractor.
Extension of time	Period of time defined by the contract administrator when setting a new date for completion of the contract (the extended completion date).
Feasibility study	A study carried out to test project concepts in relation to a particular site or building.
Final account	The account that incorporates all the authorised adjustments to the contract sum, required to be settled in a fixed period after practical completion.
Final design	The design stage in which the overall design arrangements are settled and agreed, immediately prior to detailed design stage.
Handover	The process of passing the competed building from the contractor to the client.
Inception	The stage when the broad concepts and project options are being explored.
Liquidated and ascertained damages (LADs)	A predetermined sum of money, specified in the contract documents, to which the client is entitled in the event of the contractor not completing the works within the contract period (including any extensions).
Mobilisation period	The time that elapses between the contractor being given an order to proceed and the date for possession of the site.
Named subcontractors or suppliers	A subcontractor or supplier named in a list in the tender documents as suitable to carry out the works, from which the contractor must seek tenders.
Nominated subcontractor/ supplier	A subcontractor/supplier who has been nominated by the client under the terms of the contract, with whom the contractor must place a subcontract/order.
Option appraisal	The process of considering project options at the inception stage of a project. These options may include non-building options as well as brief/design alternatives for a construction project.

Partnering	A disciplined framework for carrying out a project in a culture of co-operation and teamwork, rather than confrontation, and for mutual pursuit of value for money in which rewards are usually geared to success (Chapter 4 – paragraphs 4.25 to 4.27).
Practical completion	The point at which a project is considered sufficiently complete to hand over to the client, and formally certified as such by the contract administrator.
Prime cost sum	A sum included in the contract for expenditure in relation to a nominated subcontract.
Principal contractor	Term used in the CDM regulations for the organisation taking responsibility for health and safety matters during construction.
Project manager	A professional responsible to the client for managing some or all aspects of the building procurement process. These might include the fulfilment of the client role, and/or co-ordinating the contribution of technical disciplines. Individual project managers can come from a range of professional backgrounds. The role is often combined with others, particularly that of leader of the design team (see Chapter 2 – Box 2A).
Project scope	The definition of the extent, and the essential ingredients, of a project.
Project sponsor	A senior person in the client department – often the director – with responsibility for leading and managing the client role; the authority to take day-to-day decisions; and access to people who are making key decisions (see Chapter 2 – Box 2A).
Provisional quantities	Items in the Bill of Quantities for pieces of work that have been measured on a nominal basis for the purpose of getting prices and rates.
Provisional sum	Sums included in the contract to cover items that have not been sufficiently measured or described to be priced by the contractor.
Quantity surveyor (QS)	A professional traditionally associated with the measurement of quantities in building work to provide a basis for tendering, but now frequently providing *cost consultancy* services to

	the client and technical team on a range of financial and contractual issues.
RIBA work stages	A description of the work stages in a construction project as described by the Royal Institute of British Architects (see Appendix 6).
Risk management	See Chapter 7.
Scheme design	Design stage in which design is developed from outline proposals to the point at which spatial arrangements, character and cost can be agreed.
Site meeting	Meeting between the contractor and the contract administrator to review progress.
Specialist contractors	Contractors who provided specialist services or components including design of their elements of the work, usually as subcontractors or suppliers to the principal contractor.
Structural engineer	Designer of the elements of structures that require specialist calculations to ensure their performance in bearing loads.
Tender period	The period of time allowed for the tenderers to price and return their bids.
Tendering – single stage	Process in which contractors are invited to tender on complete information, with a view to starting construction after selection and appointment.
Tendering – two stage	Process in which contractors are invited to tender upon preliminary, indicative information, following which the design is developed in consultation with the succesful contractor, in the course of which firm contract prices are negotiated, and firm contract documentation is drawn up.
Value engineering	See Chapter 3 – paragraphs 3.16 and 3.17.
Value management	See Chapter 3 – paragraphs 3.7 and 3.8.
Variation	An instruction by the contract administrator which varies the work from that described in the contract documents.

References

1. Audit Commission, *Just Capital – Local Authority Management of Capital Projects*, Audit Commision/HMSO, 1996.

2. Final Report by Sir Michael Latham of the Government/Industry Review of Procurement and Contractual Arrangements in the UK Construction Industry, *Constructing the Team*, HMSO, 1994.

3. *Setting New Standards, A Strategy for Government Procurement*, Cm 2840, HMSO, 1995.

4. The Housing Grants, Construction and Regeneration Act, 1996.

5. Audit Commission, *Local Authority Property – a Management Handbook*, Audit Commission/HMSO, 1988.

6. Chartered Institute of Public Finance and Accountancy, *Accounting for Capital Finance: Capital Accounting Arrangements under Part IV of the Local Government and Housing Act 1989*, CIPFA, 1996.

7. Construction Industry Research and Information Association, *Value Management in UK Practice*, CIRIA 1996.

8. The Chartered Institue of Public Finance and Accountancy, *A New Guide to the Use of Capital Accounting to Improve Asset Management and Service Performance*, CIPFA, Spring 1997.

9. Construction Industry Board, *Selecting Consultants for the Team: Balancing Quality and Price*, Thomas Telford Publishing, July 1996.

10. Construction Industry Research Association, *Value by Competition: A Guide to the Competitive Procurement of Consultancy Services for Construction*, CIRIA, 1995.

11. Association of Metropolitan Authorities and Local Government Management Board, *Going Public in Europe: A Guide to the EC Public Procurement Directives*, LGMB, 1993.

12. Joint Department of the Environment (5/96) and Welsh Office (11/96) circular, *Guidance on the Conduct of Compulsory Competitive Tendering*, HMSO, April 1996.

13. Department of the Environment and the European Constuction Institute (ECI), *Partnering in the Public Sector: A Toolkit for the Implementation of Post-Award Project-Specific Partnering*, ECI, February/March 1997.

14. Department for Education and Employment Quarterly Report, *Education Building Projects: Information on Costs and Performance Data*, published quarterly.

15. Construction Industry Research and Information Association, Control of Risk: *A Guide to the Systematic Management of Risk in Construction*, CIRIA, 1995.

Index References are to paragraph numbers, Boxes and Case Studies.